# Target
## Get back on track

G

## AQA GCSE (9–1)
# English Literature
# An Inspector Calls

Julie Hughes

Published by Pearson Education Limited, 80 Strand, London, WC2R ORL.
www.pearsonschoolsandfecolleges.co.uk


Typeset by Tech-Set Ltd, Gateshead



First published 2017

20 19 18 17
10 9 8 7 6 5 4 3 2 1

**British Library Cataloguing in Publication Data**
A catalogue record for this book is available from the British Library

ISBN 978 1 292 23002 3



Printed in Italy by LEGO S.p.A

**Acknowledgements**
Quotations from An Inspector Calls by J B Priestley (Harlow, UK: Heinemann, 1992) © J B Priestley 1945. Reproduced by permission of Penguin Books Ltd and United Agents on behalf of the Estate of J B Priestley.

# Contents

# 1 Getting the plot straight

This unit will help you to understand and remember the plot of *An Inspector Calls*. The skills you will build are to:

- remember the sequence of key events in the play
- understand the significance of the structure of the play
- select the most significant events for an exam question.

In the exam you will face questions like the ones below. At the end of the unit you will plan your own response to one of these questions.

**Exam-style question**

How does Eric change in *An Inspector Calls*?

Write about:

- how Eric responds to his family and to the Inspector
- how Priestley presents Eric by the ways he writes.

**(30 marks)**
**AO4 (4 marks)**

**Exam-style question**

How does Priestley explore youth in *An Inspector Calls*?

Write about:

- the ideas about youth in *An Inspector Calls*
- how Priestley presents these ideas by the ways he writes.

**(30 marks)**
**AO4 (4 marks)**

**Before you tackle these questions, you will work through three key questions in the skills boosts to help you get the plot of *An Inspector Calls* straight.**

**How do I make sure I know the plot?**

**2 How can I explore the structure of the play?**

**3 How do I know which are the most significant events in the play?**

Read the start of one student's plan on page 2 for the **second** exam-style question above (about youth).

**Think about whether the student is:** ✓

- using specific events as evidence ☐
- showing an understanding of the way the play is structured ☐
- planning to use the most appropriate events as evidence. ☐

## Get started

**Exam-style question**

How does Priestley explore youth in *An Inspector Calls*?

Write about:

- the ideas about youth in *An Inspector Calls*
- how Priestley presents these ideas by the ways he writes. **(30 marks)**

**AO4 (4 marks)**

| Key point | Evidence |
|---|---|
| 1. The older characters are shown as self-satisfied at the start. | • Birling is full of his own importance when the Inspector first arrives: 'I was an alderman for years.'<br>• Birling boasts about his potential knighthood. |
| 2. Mr and Mrs Birling try to dominate the young people. | • Mrs Birling tries to dominate. |
| 3. Young people are shown as shallow, irresponsible and egotistical at the start. | • Sheila is shallow. |
| 4. Youth is shown as capable of change. | • Sheila is shown to change as she becomes strong enough to hear the full story. She insists on being present when Gerald is questioned, despite her mother telling her to leave: 'I wouldn't miss it for worlds.' |
| 5. Youth is shown as becoming responsible – they represent hope. | |

1. The evidence the student uses for key points 2 and 3 is too general. Note down specific details from the plot that could be added to fully support these key points.

**Key point 2:** ..........

..........

**Key point 3:** ..........

..........

2. Underline the key points that show an understanding of the structure of the play.

3. **a** There is no supporting evidence for key point 5. Tick the sentence below that you think is the most significant to support this point.

   **a** Sheila points out when the Inspector leaves that her parents 'don't seem to have learnt anything' from his visit. ☐

   **b** Sheila refuses to take part in a toast 'to us' once the hoax is revealed. ☐

   **c** Eric agrees with Sheila that he is frightened by their parents' reaction to the hoax. ☐

   **b** Write **one** sentence explaining your choice.

..........

..........

# How do I make sure I know the plot?

One way to make sure you know the plot of *An Inspector Calls* is to focus on the characters and the part they each played in the death of Eva Smith.

1. Look at this list of characters in the play.

| | | | | | | | |
|---|---|---|---|---|---|---|---|
| Arthur Birling | ☐ | Sheila Birling | ☐ | Edna | ☐ | Inspector Goole | ☐ |
| Mrs Birling | ☐ | Eric Birling | ☐ | Gerald Croft | ☐ | Eva Smith | ☐ |

a. Five of the characters listed are questioned by the Inspector. In what order are they questioned? Number them from **1** to **5**.

b. Cross out ~~cat~~ the name of the character who does not actually appear in the play.

c. Priestley gives very detailed stage directions at the start of the play. Write **two** sentences explaining how these directions help the audience to see that the Birlings are in a relaxed mood as the play opens.

..........

..........

2. Read these quotations from Act I. They all establish the wealth and social position of the Birling family.

a. Which quotation best introduces the Birlings' social status? Tick ✓ your choice.

| | ✓ |
|---|---|
| 'Tell cook from me' | ☐ |
| 'I was Lord Mayor here two years ago' | ☐ |
| 'Just a knighthood, of course' | ☐ |

b. Write **one** sentence explaining your choice.

..........

..........

3. Think about the role played by the Birling and Croft characters in the fate of Eva Smith. Put this timeline of Eva's life in order by numbering the events **1** to **5** and adding the name of the character responsible for each event.

| Order of events | Events | Character responsible |
|---|---|---|
| | Eva changes her name to Daisy Renton and starts a relationship with a man. She moves away when he breaks off the relationship. | |
| | Eva meets a man in Brumley and gets pregnant. He steals money to support her. | |
| | Eva works at Milwards until she is sacked because of a complaint about her. | |
| | Eva asks for help from the Brumley Women's Charity but is refused. | |
| | Eva organises a strike at Birling and Company and is sacked. | |

##  How can I explore the structure of the play?

One way to explore the structure of the play is to consider how Priestley raises and lowers the tension as the characters are questioned about their part in Eva's death.

1. Look at some of the key events from Acts I and II in *An Inspector Calls*.

| | Act I |
|---|---|
| | Arthur Birling makes a toast to the engagement. |
| | Arthur Birling dismisses the idea of a war with Germany. |
| | The Inspector arrives. |
| | Sheila runs from the room crying. |
| | The Inspector leaves with Eric. |
| | **End of Act I:** Sheila warns Gerald that the Inspector knows everything. |
| | **Act II** |
| | Gerald encourages Sheila to leave. |
| | Mrs Birling enters, unaware of what has happened. |
| | Gerald reveals details of his affair with Eva. |
| | The Inspector reveals that Eva was pregnant. |
| | Mrs Birling says that the baby's father is entirely to blame. |
| | Eric enters. |

a. The tension rises and falls through Acts I and II. Number the events in each act from **1** to **5**, with **5** being a point of maximum tension for the audience.

b. Select **one** of the events you have marked as 5. Write **one** or **two** sentences explaining how it creates tension for the audience.

........................................................................................................

........................................................................................................

2. At the end of Act III, the tension lightens and the events are carefully structured to create doubt about the Inspector.

a. Number the following events in the correct order (**1** to **4**).

| | End of Act III |
|---|---|
| | Mr Birling rings Chief Constable Roberts. |
| | Sheila questions whether Goole was really an Inspector. |
| | Gerald rings the infirmary. |
| | Eric and Mr Birling argue about the stolen money. |

b. Write **one** or **two** sentences explaining the effect of this structure on the audience.

........................................................................................................

........................................................................................................

## 3 How do I know which are the most significant events in the play?

What makes an event or speech significant in *An Inspector Calls* will depend on the focus of the question you are answering.

1. Look at these key events from Act I, which can all be linked to the idea of youth in the play.

   a. Match each event to the correct explanation by drawing lines between them.

|  |  |
|---|---|
| **A** Mr Birling lectures Eric and Gerald about the state of the world | **a** Shows he is immature and slightly drunk, which is disrespectful |
| **B** Eric suddenly bursts out laughing | **b** Suggests she is an obedient daughter, which is a traditional role for young women |
| **C** Sheila apologises to her father for not listening | **c** Shows he is in charge and feels that younger people should listen to the experience of their elders |

   b. Which event do you think is is the most significant? Number them **1** to **3**, with **1** being the most significant.

2. The events below from later in the play can also be linked to the idea of youth.

|  | | |
|---|---|---|
| Mrs Birling is shocked when she hears Eric regularly drinks too much. | ☐ | ☐ |
| Eric challenges his father by suggesting the girls were right to go on strike. | ☐ | ☐ |
| Eric is aggressive towards his mother, accusing her of killing his unborn child. | ☐ | ☐ |
| Eric shows distress and shame over his part in Eva's fate. | ☐ | ☐ |

   a. Which event do you think is the most significant? Number them from **1** to **4**, with **1** being most significant.

   b. Write **one** sentence explaining the link between youth and the event you numbered.

   ..........

   ..........

3. Look again at the events from later in the play in question **2**. They can also be linked to the question about how Eric changes.

   a. Which do you think is the most significant event for a question about Eric changing? Label them **A** to **D**, with **A** being most significant.

   b. Write **two** sentences explaining what your most significant chosen event suggests about the way Eric changes.

   ..........

   ..........

   ..........

# Getting the plot straight

To be sure of writing an effective response about *An Inspector Calls*, you need to:

- know the key events in the play and the order in which they happen
- understand how the plot is sequenced to create tension
- understand how to select the most significant events for a question.

Look again at this exam-style question from the start of the unit.

**Exam-style question**

How does Eric change in *An Inspector Calls*?

Look at one student's planning notes in response to this question.

*Eric is first presented as immature.*

- *He is described in the stage directions as 'not quite at ease'.*
- *He is slightly drunk and suddenly bursts out laughing for no reason [gives hint to audience that he might be an unpredictable character].*
- *He interrupts his father [creates tension for audience].*

*Eric challenges traditional values in Act I.*

- *He challenges his father about Birling's sacking of Eva.*
- *He shows sympathy for Eva and suggests girls like her should be able to try for higher wages [this hints to audience that he might change].*

*[Eric off stage for Act II – allows tension to build about his part in Eva's fate. Returns at start of Act III and is last to be questioned – would suggest to audience that his part in her fate is important.]*

*Eric starts to show remorse/take responsibility.*

- *He admits he treated Eva badly and exploited her sexually.*
- *He admits he stole money for her.*
- *He expresses regret that he couldn't help Eva more.*

*Eric has changed by end of play.*

- *He agrees with Sheila that their parents' reaction is frightening – suggests to audience that he is capable of changing.*

1. Think about all the ideas this student has included in their plan.

   Annotate the plan, highlighting and labelling all the different elements that will make the student's response successful.

# Your turn!

You are now going to **plan your own answer** in response to the other exam-style question you saw at the beginning of this unit.

**Exam-style question**

How does Priestley explore youth in *An Inspector Calls*?

1. Put these plot details in the correct order by numbering them from **1** to **10**.

| Plot detail | Number | ✓ / ✗ |
|---|---|---|
| Sheila tells her father not to interfere in her engagement. | | |
| Mr Birling is told Eva has killed herself using bleach. | | |
| Eric agrees with Sheila that their parents' reaction is frightening. | | |
| Mr Birling relaxes when the Inspector has gone and pours drinks. | | |
| Mrs Birling tells Sheila not to contradict her. | | |
| Eric is drunk at the celebratory party. | | |
| Gerald tries to give back the engagement ring. | | |
| Sheila accuses her parents of being childish by not facing facts. | | |
| Mrs Birling insists the father of the unborn child is to blame. | | |
| Mr Birling calls the *Titanic* 'unsinkable'. | | |

2. Which of the plot details above are not relevant to the question? Put a cross ✗ by them.
3. Which of the plot details suggest that young people represent hope at the end of the play? Circle (A) them and add appropriate quotations underneath.
4. Which **three** plot details are the most significant for this question? Tick ✓ them.
5. Select **one** of the details you identified in question 4.
   a. Add an appropriate quotation.
   b. Write **two** sentences on paper explaining why the detail is significant.

# Review your skills

## Check up

Review your planning notes for the exam-style question on page 7. Tick the column to show how well you think you have done each of the following.

| | Not quite | Nearly there | Got it! |
|---|---|---|---|
| shown an understanding of the sequence of events in the play | ☐ | ☐ | ☐ |
| shown an understanding of the structure of the play | ☐ | ☐ | ☐ |
| selected the most significant plot details to explore the theme of youth in the play | ☐ | ☐ | ☐ |

Look over all of your work in this unit. Note down **three** points to remember when considering the plot of *An Inspector Calls*.

1. ........................................................................

2. ........................................................................

3. ........................................................................

## Need more practice?

Now use your planning notes to write a response to this exam-style question.

### Exam-style question

How does Priestley explore youth in *An Inspector Calls*?

Write about:

- the ideas about youth in *An Inspector Calls*
- how Priestley presents these ideas by the ways he writes.

(30 marks)

AO4 (4 marks)

Start by noting down which plot details from the play you would choose to write about in your response to this question.

How confident do you feel about each of these **skills?** Colour in the bars.

1. How do I make sure I know the plot?
2. How can I explore the structure of the play?
3. How do I know which are the most significant events in the play?

# Exploring character

This unit will help you to understand how characters are presented in *An Inspector Calls* and how to develop your response to them. The skills you will build are to:

- understand the presentation of characters in the play
- explore the development of characters in the play
- link characters to the themes of the play.

In the exam you will face questions like the ones below. At the end of the unit you will plan and write one or two paragraphs in response to one of these questions.

**Exam-style question**

How and why does Sheila change in *An Inspector Calls*?

Write about:

- how Sheila responds to her family and to the Inspector
- how Priestley presents Sheila by the ways he writes.

**(30 marks)**
**AO4 (4 marks)**

**Exam-style question**

How does Priestley explore power in *An Inspector Calls*?

Write about:

- the ideas about power in *An Inspector Calls*
- how Priestley presents these ideas by the ways he writes.

**(30 marks)**
**AO4 (4 marks)**

**Before you tackle these questions, you will work through three key questions in the skills boosts to help you explore the play's characters.**

**How do I make sure I know the characters?**

**How do I track the development of a character?**

**How do I link characters to themes?**

Read one student's notes on page 10 on the **second** exam-style question above (about power).

**As you read these notes, think about how the student tries to understand the character of Arthur Birling. Has the student:** ✓

- shown an understanding of how Arthur Birling is presented ☐
- shown an understanding of how his character is developed ☐
- selected relevant events and speeches to comment on? ☐

**Exam-style question**

How does Priestley explore power in *An Inspector Calls*?

Write about:

- the ideas about power in *An Inspector Calls*
- how Priestley presents these ideas by the ways he writes. **(30 marks)**

**AO4 (4 marks)**

| *Getting to know Arthur Birling and how he uses power* | |
|---|---|
| *My ideas* | *Evidence* |
| *At start of play, he is:*<br>• *self-satisfied*<br>• *confident*<br>• *greedy*<br>• *powerful.* | • *Boasts about knighthood*<br>• *Sits symbolically at one end of table*<br>• *Has most lines before Inspector turns up*<br>• *Lectures Gerald and Eric, calls them 'youngsters'* |
| *As play develops, he becomes:*<br>• *arrogant – misuses his power*<br>• *callous – misuses his power.* | • *Assumes Inspector will feel inferior to his status*<br>• *Shows no guilt about Eva; calls her 'that girl'* |
| *At the end – power shown to be dangerous*<br>*He is:*<br>• *dishonest*<br>• *selfish*<br>• *cruel.* | • *Wants to cover up theft of money*<br>• *Cares more about public scandal than Eva's life*<br>• *When Inspector goes he jokes about the events, 'You'll have a good laugh over it' (Act III)* |
| *At the end of the play he is unchanged – still feels powerful.* | |

1. Which piece of evidence best supports the student's idea that Arthur starts the play as a powerful man? Write **one** sentence explaining your choice.

..........

..........

2. The student has decided that Arthur Birling remains unchanged. Which of the events used as evidence best supports this point? Write **one** sentence explaining your choice.

..........

..........

3. The question is about the theme of power. Which of the following other themes could be linked to the student's point about Arthur Birling's confidence? Tick your choice(s).

responsibility ☐ reputation ☐ inequality ☐

## How do I make sure I know the characters?

To write effectively about characters it is helpful to look at the start of *An Inspector Calls*. This is the point at which characters are established for the audience. You should also consider the stage directions.

1. Think about how the character of Sheila is presented at the start of the play. In Act I Sheila is described as:

'very pleased with life and rather excited'

talking 'gaily, possessively' to Gerald

so busy admiring her engagement ring she stops listening to her father

'attentive' to her father after apologising for not listening

How would you sum up the character of Sheila in Act I? Tick any of the words below and/or add your own ideas.

| shallow | | immature | | sheltered | | | |
|---|---|---|---|---|---|---|---|
| obedient | | traditional | | | | | |

2. Now think about how the Inspector is presented to the audience when he first appears in Act I.

described as projecting an 'impression of massiveness'

the lights get 'brighter and harder' when he arrives

cuts into Mr Birling's impatient question about why he is there

looks hard at those he questions

How would you sum up the character of the Inspector in Act I? Tick any of the words below and/or add your own ideas.

| powerful | | confident | | unimpressed | | | |
|---|---|---|---|---|---|---|---|
| impatient | | commanding | | | | | |

3. Think about how the characters in *An Inspector Calls* first respond to the news in Act I that Eva Smith has died from drinking bleach.

Mr Birling: 'Horrid business. But I don't understand why you should come here…'

Eric: 'My God!'

Sheila: 'Oh – how horrible! Was it an accident?'

Gerald: 'Look here, sir. Wouldn't you rather I was out of this?'

How would you sum up their reactions? Select **one** word from below for each character or add one of your own.

arrogant uncaring shocked sympathetic indifferent callous

| Mr Birling | | Eric | |
|---|---|---|---|
| Sheila | | Gerald | |

## 2 How do I track the development of a character?

The structure of *An Inspector Calls* hinges on how characters react to the news about Eva Smith and whether they change as a result of what they hear about her fate. To track a character's development, think about how they respond to the news about Eva throughout the play.

1. Think about how Sheila is presented at key moments in the play.

| | | |
|---|---|---|
| **Act I** Wishes she hadn't been told about Eva's death | **Act I** Shows remorse for treating Eva badly | **Act II** Warns her mother that the Inspector knows everything |
| **Act II** Finds it hard to accept responsibility for Eva's suicide 'I can't believe' | **Act III** After Inspector goes, criticises parents for not changing | **Act III** Remembers the Inspector's warnings and is frightened |

a. Circle the **three** most significant moments that suggest a change in Sheila's character.

b. Complete these **two** sentences summing up how Sheila's character changes during the course of the play.

*Sheila's initial reaction to the news about Eva is sympathy, but she soon wishes she hadn't been told. This suggests* ..........

*However, by the end of the play* ..........

..........

2. The Birling family and Gerald all played a part in Eva's death but by the end of the play only some of them have been changed by what they have heard. Add the characters', names along the scale to show how they have changed at the end of the play.

no change | slight remorse | some remorse | extreme remorse

.......... .......... .......... ..........

3. Consider how the Inspector remains mysterious throughout the play. Look at these events from Acts II and III.

**Act II** The Inspector comments that 'we often' make an impression on the young ones.

**Act II** The Inspector shows the photograph to Mrs Birling then takes it back.

**Act III** It is revealed that there is no Inspector Goole on the police force.

Use one of these events to write **one** sentence explaining how it makes the Inspector appear mysterious.

..........

..........

## 3 How do I link characters to themes?

Priestley uses the character of the Inspector to force the Birling family and Gerald Croft to examine their behaviour. This allows the audience to think about right and wrong in society. When writing your responses, it is a good idea to consider how characters can be linked through their actions and words to these key ideas, or themes.

① Responsibility is one of the key themes of *An Inspector Calls*. Complete these notes to show how Priestley uses characters to give audiences ideas about this theme.

| | |
|---|---|
| *Act I: **Inspector** says that people should put themselves in the position of girls like Eva.* | *Introduces idea of social responsibility* |
| *Act I: **Mr Birling** says 'It's my duty to keep labour costs down'.* | *Represents wealthy middle class. Has no social responsibility. Feels* |
| *Act II: **Sybil Birling** says that Eva did not seem to be a deserving case for her charity.* | |
| *Act I: **Sheila Birling** admits that she used her social status to get Eva dismissed from Milwards.* | |

② Priestley uses the character of Sheila to show how people can develop a sense of responsibility.

**a** Which of the following quotations best shows that Sheila develops a sense of social responsibility over the course of the play? Tick your choice.

| | | ✓ |
|---|---|---|
| Act III | 'Between us we drove that girl to commit suicide' | ☐ |
| Act III | 'I had her turned out of a job' | ☐ |
| Act III | 'So there's nothing to be sorry for, nothing to learn …' | ☐ |

**b** Write **one** sentence explaining your choice.

.................................................................................................

③ Look at the key events involving Arthur Birling, then look at the themes below. Beside each event, write the theme that links to it.

| | | |
|---|---|---|
| Act I | Arthur tells Sybil to thank 'cook'. | |
| Act I | Arthur expresses regret that Gerald's parents can't be at the party. | |
| Act III | Arthur worries that he will lose his chance of a knighthood. | |

reputation love equality age

# Exploring character

To explore how the characters are presented in *An Inspector Calls* you need to:

- think about how they are described and what they say at the start of the play
- consider how they react to the Inspector and whether they change as a result
- link them to themes of the play.

Look again at this exam-style question from the start of the unit.

**Exam-style question**

How and why does Sheila change in *An Inspector Calls*?

Look at these two paragraphs from a student's response to this question.

*At the start of the play, Priestley presents Sheila as rather shallow. She is described mainly in terms of her appearance, as a 'pretty girl'. She appears to be more interested in admiring her engagement ring than in listening to her father talk about serious issues. She is also presented as very traditional: she is obedient to her father as she apologises for her lack of attention; and she calls her parents 'Mummy' and 'Daddy'.*

*However, Priestley gives the audience early hints that Sheila may change. She upsets her mother's rather snobbish values as the first of the family to show any sadness about the death of Eva, although her initial reaction is still rather shallow as she thinks of it in terms of the way it has spoiled her evening, declaring 'I wish you hadn't told me.' As the interrogation of Arthur Birling progresses, her interest in what happened to Eva intensifies and she begins to challenge her father, by 'cutting in' when he is trying to placate the Inspector. Her emerging sense of responsibility then becomes evident as she tells her father that sacking Eva was a 'mean' thing to do.*

1. **a** Underline any phrases in the first paragraph that show this student understands how Sheila is presented at the start of the play. Label them **'Presentation'**.

   **b** Highlight in green any links the student has made to the way the play is structured. Label them **'Plot'**.

   **c** Circle where the student has shown an understanding of how Sheila changes. Label them **'Changes'**.

   **d** Highlight in yellow any links the student has made to the themes of social class and responsibility. Label them **'Themes'**.

2. Which of the following themes could also be linked to Sheila in these paragraphs? Annotate the student's response with your ideas.

| age | reputation | power | equality |
|---|---|---|---|

# Your turn!

You are now going to **write your own two paragraphs** in response to this exam-style question.

**Exam-style question**

How and why does Sheila change in *An Inspector Calls*?

Complete these tasks to make notes for your answer.

1. Gather notes about how Sheila is presented at the start of the play, up until the Inspector arrives. Remember to consider stage directions.

2. Gather notes about how Sheila's character develops in Acts I and II. Remember to consider how her reaction to Eva's fate suggests she will change.

3. Gather notes about how Sheila is presented in Act III. Consider how the audience is shown that she is the character who changes the most.

4. a Go back over your notes and make further notes on the following themes, and/or your own themes.

   age | social responsibility | equality

   b Use your planning to write **two** paragraphs in response to the exam-style question above on paper.

# Review your skills

### Check up

Review your response to the exam-style question on page 15. Tick ✓ the column to show how well you think you have done each of the following.

| | Not quite ✓ | Nearly there ✓ | Got it! ✓ |
|---|---|---|---|
| shown an understanding of how Sheila is presented at key points in the play | ☐ | ☐ | ☐ |
| shown an understanding of how Sheila's character develops throughout the play | ☐ | ☐ | ☐ |
| linked Sheila's character to key themes in the play | ☐ | ☐ | ☐ |

Look over all of your work in this unit. Note down ✎ **three** important things to remember when exploring the presentation of a character in *An Inspector Calls*.

1. ..........

2. ..........

3. ..........

## Need more practice?

Try writing ✎ **two** paragraphs of an answer to the **second** question you saw on page 9.

### Exam-style question

How does Priestley explore power in *An Inspector Calls*?

Think about:

- how Arthur Birling is presented at the start of the play, including stage directions
- how he reacts to the Inspector's questioning and to Eva's fate
- how he can be linked to power and any other themes.

How confident do you feel about each of these **skills?** Colour ✎ in the bars.

# 3 Exploring themes

This unit will help you to understand and explore how the themes of *An Inspector Calls* are presented in the play. The skills you will build are to:

- identify the themes in the play
- comment on the development of themes in the play
- link themes to character, setting and structure.

In the exam you will face questions like the ones below. At the end of the unit you will plan and write one or two paragraphs in response to one of these questions.

**Exam-style question**

How does Priestley explore responsibility in *An Inspector Calls*?

Write about:

- the ideas about responsibility in *An Inspector Calls*
- how Priestley presents these ideas by the ways he writes. **(30 marks)**

**AO4 (4 marks)**

**Exam-style question**

How does Priestley use the character of Arthur Birling to explore ideas about power in *An Inspector Calls*?

Write about:

- how Priestley presents Arthur Birling
- how Priestley uses the character to explore ideas about power. **(30 marks)**

**AO4 (4 marks)**

**Before you tackle these questions, you will work through three key questions in the skills boosts to help you explore the themes in *An Inspector Calls*.**

**How do I identify the themes of the play?**

**How do I track the development of a theme?**

**How do I link themes to character, setting and structure?**

Look at one student's notes on page 18 on the **first** exam-style question above (about responsibility).

**As you read these notes, think about whether the student has:**

- shown an understanding of the way responsibility is shown in the play ☐
- tracked and commented on the development of responsibility in the play ☐
- linked responsibility to appropriate characters, settings and plot details. ☐

## Get started

**Exam-style question**

How does Priestley explore responsibility in *An Inspector Calls*?

| | |
|---|---|
| *Introduction* | • *Priestley presents responsibility as important.*<br>• *He uses the play to show that people in society should take responsibility for those who are less fortunate.* |
| *Responsibility presented as lacking in higher classes* | • *Mr Birling feels his responsibility is to make large profits.*<br>• *He makes a speech at the start about man having to look after himself.*<br>• *Mr and Mrs Birling don't change.* |
| *Inspector presents responsibility as important* | • *The Inspector is used to show this.*<br>• *He says: 'We don't live alone. We are members of one body. We are responsible for each other.' (Act III)* |
| *Inspector questions each character in turn to build a picture of how they showed no responsibility for Eva* | • *Mr Birling sacked her and calls her 'that girl'. (Act I)*<br>• *Sheila had her dismissed. (Act I)*<br>• *Mrs Birling refused to help her. (Act II)* |
| *Sheila and Eric start to take responsibility for their actions* | • *Sheila shows guilt when questioned: 'I'll never, never do it again.' (Act I)*<br>• *Eric says: 'the girl's dead and we all helped to kill her'. (Act III)*<br>• *Suggests young people will take responsibility in future.* |

1. Underline (A) and label (pencil) where the student has shown an understanding of:
   - a link between **character** and **responsibility**
   - a link between **structure** and **responsibility**

2. Which of the following events could also be linked to the point about the Inspector presenting responsibility as important? Tick (✓) your choice.

   - **Act I** The Inspector interrupts Arthur Birling. ☐
   - **Act II** The Inspector insists Gerald stay while Arthur is questioned. ☐
   - **Act III** The Inspector refuses to show Gerald the photograph. ☐

## How do I identify the themes of the play?

In *An Inspector Calls* Priestley raises some of his key ideas about how people should live. These key ideas are called 'themes' and it is important that you can identify them in your responses. To do this, start by considering Eva's story. First, think about the ideas it presents to the audience. Then go on to consider key events and speeches in the play.

**1** Look at some of the key themes from *An Inspector Calls* and key events in Eva's story.

| | |
|---|---|
| **A** Responsibility | **a** Eva is sacked for organising a strike at the factory. |
| **B** Morality | **b** Gerald breaks off his relationship with Eva. |
| **C** Power | **c** Mrs Birling turns Eva away from her charity. |
| **D** Equality | **d** Sheila uses her social status to get Eva dismissed from Milwards. |
| **E** Love | **e** Eva commits suicide. |

**a** What idea does each event raise for the audience? Draw lines to match the events to the themes. Some events may link to more than one theme.

**b** Select and highlight **one** event. Annotate it with your ideas about how it can be linked to one of the themes.

**2** Some key speeches in the play can be linked to more than one theme. Read Arthur Birling's speech from the start of Act I.

> **Birling:** (*solemnly*) But this is the point. I don't want to lecture you two young fellows again. But what so many of you don't seem to understand now, when things are so much easier, is that a man has to make his own way – has to look after himself – and his family too, of course, when he has one – and so long as he does that he won't come to much harm. But the way some of these cranks talk and write now, you'd think everybody has to look after everybody else, as if we were all mixed up together like bees in a hive – community and all that nonsense. But take my word for it, you youngsters – and I've learnt in the good hard school of experience – that a man has to mind his own business and look after himself and his own …

**a** Tick any of the themes below that can be linked to Birling's speech.

responsibility ☐ morality ☐ power ☐ equality ☐

**b** For **two** of the themes, annotate the speech to explain the links you have made.

## 2 How do I track the development of a theme?

You can explore how themes develop in *An Inspector Calls* by considering how they are presented in different parts of the play.

1. Look at some of the key points in Act I, where Priestley introduces the idea of power.

   - Arthur Birling talks about employers coming together to protect their interests.
   - Arthur Birling tells the Inspector that he used to be Lord Mayor.
   - Arthur Birling tells the Inspector he told the strikers to 'clear out'.
   - The Inspector accuses Sheila of using her power as a valued customer to get Eva dismissed.

   **a** How does Priestley present power in this act of the play? Tick any of the ideas below.

   ☐ as belonging to the middle classes ☐ as dangerous ☐ as positive
   ☐ as corrupting ☐ as necessary ☐ as taken for granted ☐ as negative

   **b** Write a sentence explaining **one** of your ideas.

   ..................................................................................

   ..................................................................................

2. Now consider these two statements about how power is presented later in the play.

   **Statement 1**

   *The power shifts from Mr and Mrs Birling to the Inspector.*

   **Statement 2**

   *The power shifts from Arthur and Sybil Birling to their children.*

   **a** Tick any of the key events below you think are most relevant as evidence for these **Statement 1**.

   | Key event 1 | Key event 2 | Key event 3 |
   |---|---|---|
   | ☐ **Act III:** The Inspector tells Arthur to 'stop'. He is described as 'taking charge masterfully', with other characters falling silent. | ☐ **Act III:** Arthur pours himself a drink as soon as the Inspector has left. | ☐ **Act III:** The telephone interrupts Arthur when he is saying that the younger generation can't take a joke. |

   **b** For **Statement 2**, write **one** sentence explaining what Priestley wants the audience to feel about power at that point in the play.

   ..................................................................................

   ..................................................................................

3. Complete these sentences to show how the presentation of power changes as the play progresses.

   *At the start, power is shown to belong to the middle classes when* .................................................. .

   *However, later in the play,* ..................................................................................

   ..................................................................................

   ..................................................................................

## How do I link themes to character, setting and structure?

When you answer a theme question you should select the most significant points from the play as evidence for your ideas. You will also need to think about how Priestley links themes to his characters, the setting and the structure of the play.

1. What does Priestley suggest through his themes? Complete the table to show:
   - a which characters and themes link together
   - b which key event best supports each link.

| Theme | Character | Key event |
|---|---|---|
| **Reputation** – shows that it is more important to middle class than taking responsibility for others in society. | Mr Birling | In Act III he is more concerned about a potential scandal than about Eva's fate. |
| **Responsibility** – suggests everybody should care for others and think carefully about their actions. | | |
| **Equality** – shows that a lack of equality makes working class lives very difficult. | | |

2. Think about the setting of *An Inspector Calls*. Read this extract from the stage directions at the start of the play.

> At rise of curtain, the four BIRLINGS and GERALD are seated at the table, with ARTHUR BIRLING at one end, his wife at the other, ERIC downstage and SHEILA and GERALD seated upstage. EDNA, the parlourmaid, is just clearing the table, which has no cloth, of dessert plates and champagne glasses, etc., and then replacing them with a decanter of port, cigar box and cigarettes. Port glasses are already on the table.

   - a Which of the following themes can be linked to this extract? Tick your choices.

   equality ☐ respectability ☐ power ☐ exploitation ☐ responsibility ☐

   - b For **one** of your choices, underline where in the extract the theme is evident.

3. Think about the structure of the play.

   Complete the table to show what each stage of Eva's story suggests about responsibility.

| Stages of Eva's story | Suggested responsibility |
|---|---|
| **Stage 1:** Sheila admits she used her social position to get Eva dismissed. | |
| **Stage 2:** Gerald says he has no idea what happened to Eva after he broke off their relationship. | |
| **Stage 3:** Eric admits he was drunk when he first went to Eva's lodgings. | |

# Exploring themes

To explore themes in *An Inspector Calls* and write about them effectively in your responses, you need to:

- think about how key scenes and speeches are used to present Priestley's themes
- compare how themes are presented at different points in the play
- consider how characters, the setting and the structure are used to present themes.

Look again at this exam-style question you saw at the start of the unit.

**Exam-style question**

How does Priestley explore responsibility in *An Inspector Calls*?

Write about:

- the ideas about responsibility in *An Inspector Calls*
- how Priestley presents these ideas by the ways he writes. **(30 marks)**

**AO4 (4 marks)**

Look at these two paragraphs written by one student in response to this exam-style question.

*At the start of the play, Priestley suggests that the wealthy middle class has no sense of responsibility for others. This is shown through the Birlings, who are presented as wealthy by the comfortable setting and the way the play starts with a celebration of Sheila's engagement. Arthur then shows his lack of responsibility for others by telling Gerald and Eric that men should look after themselves and their families. He calls people who want to look after everybody else 'cranks', which shows he thinks the idea is ridiculous.*

*Later in Act I, Arthur also shows that he takes no responsibility for the welfare of his workers. When questioned by the Inspector he says his only responsibility is to 'keep labour costs down'. This shows he cares more for money than he does for the people who work in his factory. He is shown as feeling no guilt and taking no responsibility for Eva's fate. Priestley wants the audience to disapprove of Arthur's view as he is presented as callous, calling Eva 'that girl' and referring to his workers as 'these people'.*

*In contrast, the Inspector* ..........................................................................................

..........................................................................................................................

1. Underline where the student has used key events to support the points made about the theme. Label them **'key events'**.

2. Circle where the student has linked characters, the setting or the structure of the play to the theme. Label them **'character'**, **'setting'** or **'structure'**.

3. The student has started a third paragraph about the Inspector. Complete the opening sentence. Try to show an understanding of how the theme of responsibility is developed through the Inspector.

# Your turn!

You are now going to **write your own answer** in response to this exam-style question.

**Exam-style question**

How does Priestley explore responsibility in *An Inspector Calls*?

Write about:

- the ideas about responsibility in *An Inspector Calls*
- how Priestley presents these ideas by the ways he writes. **(30 marks)**

**AO4 (4 marks)**

You should spend around 30 minutes on this type of question, so you should aim to write **four** or **five** paragraphs.

1. Use the table below to note down how responsibility is shown in all three acts of *An Inspector Calls*. Select **two** key events from each act.

| | Act I | Act II | Act III |
|---|---|---|---|
| Key event 1 | | | |
| Key event 2 | | | |

2. Look carefully at the events you have chosen. Do they highlight how the theme of responsibility is shown in different ways at different points in the play? Add notes to your ideas about how the theme is developed.

3. Think about characters, the setting and the structure of the play. Add notes to show how these are used to present different ideas about responsibility.

4. Use your notes to write **two** paragraphs on paper in response to this question.

# Review your skills

## Check up

Review your response to the exam-style question on page 23. Tick ✓ the column to show how well you think you have done each of the following.

| | Not quite ✓ | Nearly there ✓ | Got it! ✓ |
|---|---|---|---|
| identified key events or speeches where the theme of responsibility is presented | ☐ | ☐ | ☐ |
| commented on how the theme of responsibility is developed | ☐ | ☐ | ☐ |
| linked ideas about responsibility to characters, the setting and the structure of the play | ☐ | ☐ | ☐ |

Look over all of your work in this unit. Note down three points to remember when writing about themes in *An Inspector Calls*.

1. ..........
2. ..........
3. ..........

## Need more practice?

Here is another exam-style question, this time exploring the theme of power.

### Exam-style question

How does Priestley use the character of Arthur Birling to explore ideas about power in *An Inspector Calls*?

Write about:

- how Priestley presents Arthur Birling
- how Priestley uses the character to explore ideas about power. **(30 marks)**

AO4 (4 marks)

Plan and write a response to this question. Remember to think about how the theme is developed and whether it can be linked to any characters, the setting or the structure of the play.

How confident do you feel about each of these **skills?** Colour in the bars.

Get started

**Show understanding of the relationships between texts and the contexts in which they were written (AO3)**

# 4 Exploring context

This unit will help you to show your understanding of the play's context – its relationship with the time it was written, the time it was set and the way different audiences respond. The skills you will build are to:

- understand the relationship between the play and its context
- use relevant contextual ideas
- make relevant comments about audience responses.

In the exam you will face questions like the ones below. At the end of the unit you will plan your own response to one of these questions.

**Exam-style question**

How does Priestley explore social class in *An Inspector Calls*?

Write about:

- the ideas about social class in *An Inspector Calls*
- how Priestley presents these ideas by the ways he writes.

**(30 marks)**
**AO4 (4 marks)**

**Exam-style question**

How does Priestley use the character of Sybil Birling in *An Inspector Calls* to explore ideas about responsibility?

Write about:

- how Priestley presents Sybil
- how Priestley uses this character to explore ideas about responsibility.

**(30 marks)**
**AO4 (4 marks)**

**Before you tackle these questions, you will work through three key questions in the skills boosts to help you explore the context of *An Inspector Calls*.**

**1 How do I make sure I know the context?**

**2 How do I select relevant contextual ideas?**

**3 How do I include ideas about audience response?**

Read part of one student's notes on page 26 on the **first** exam-style question above (about social class).

**Think about whether the student has:**

- shown an understanding of the context of the play ☐
- planned to use relevant contextual ideas ☐
- shown an understanding of different audience responses. ☐

## Get started

**Exam-style question**

How does Priestley explore social class in *An Inspector Calls*?

| | |
|---|---|
| *Start of play: Priestley makes the difference in class immediately obvious – shows this is an important theme* | • *Stage directions – setting is a comfortable house, Birlings and Gerald sitting and in evening dress*<br>• *Contrast to Edna who is silently clearing the table*<br>• *Represents division of classes at the time* |
| *Arthur Birling shows distrust of w/classes* | • *Says working classes would start 'asking for the earth' so should be treated harshly*<br>• *Links to labour strikes of time play is set, when wealthy middle classes worried that spread of socialism would mean losing what they had*<br>• *Gerald agrees – suggests view was common at the time* |
| *Sybil looks down on w/classes* | • *Refers to Eva as 'that sort' when hearing about her relationship with Eric*<br>• *Reflects view at the time that working classes had lower moral standards* |

1. Underline (A) where the student has shown an understanding of the context of the play.

2. What point do you think Priestley was making about social class at the time the play was set? Write (✎) **one** or **two** sentences to explain your ideas.

...................................................................................................................

...................................................................................................................

...................................................................................................................

3. The student has not planned any comments on audience response. Select **one** of the points above and annotate (✎) it with your ideas about how a modern audience would respond.

Skills boost

## How do I make sure I know the context?

You need to be aware of all the different contexts of *An Inspector Calls* so you can make relevant comments in your responses. Contextual ideas can be historical events, or relevant beliefs and attitudes from the time the play was written and set. To help you remember key contextual ideas, you can link them to characters and themes.

**1** Look at these contextual ideas from *An Inspector Calls*. Tick ✓ any that are relevant to the play.

| ✓ | Contextual ideas, 1912 | Characters, links to context and themes |
|---|---|---|
| | *Titanic* sunk in April | |
| | No unemployment benefits | |
| | Position in society very important to Edwardians | *Arthur Birling; more concerned about reputation than Eva's fate* |
| | Coal miners' strike secured minimum wage | |
| | Women paid less than men for same job | |
| | Most married women were dependent on their husbands | |
| | J.B. Priestley went to university | |
| | Captain Scott died in the Antarctic | |
| | Suffragettes were protesting for the vote | |

**2** Think about these characters and themes:

Eva Smith | Arthur Birling | Sybil Birling | Gerald | Sheila

equality | reputation | power | responsibility | social class

Link them to the contextual ideas you ticked in question **1** by writing ✎ **one** character or **one** theme next to each idea and explaining the link.

**3** The play is set in 1912 but was written and first performed in 1945. Look again at the ideas above and think about what happened in Britain between these two dates.

How different would life have been for Eva and Sheila in 1945? Complete ✎ this table with your ideas.

Think about the way all social classes fought together in the war; how women replaced men in the workplace and won the vote in 1918; and how the welfare state was established in 1945.

| Life for Sheila | Life for Eva |
|---|---|
| | |

## 2 How do I select relevant contextual ideas?

You do not need to make contextual comments in every paragraph of your response, but any comments you *do* make must be relevant to the point you are making.

1. Read what one student wrote in answer to a question about Arthur Birling.

*Arthur Birling is presented as callous. This is shown in Act I when he is being questioned about Eva's part in the strike and he talks about coming down 'sharply' on 'these people'. This shows he cares more about profits than about the workers in his factory.*

**a** Which contextual ideas best support this point? Tick your choice.

- [ ] *Titanic* sunk in April 1912
- [ ] No unemployment benefits in 1912
- [ ] 1912 coal miners' strike secured minimum wage

**b** Write **one** sentence explaining your choice.

..............................................................................................................................

..............................................................................................................................

2. Look at one student's notes about Sybil Birling.

**defer:** let someone else decide

- *Sybil comes from a higher social position than Arthur, but she usually* ***defers*** *to him. This is shown when he asks her to pass on a message to 'cook' about the meal.*
- *Sybil is shown to be naïve about her children. She is shocked when Sheila uses the modern term 'squiffy' and has no idea about Eric's drinking.*
- *Sybil takes no responsibility for her actions. She will not take any blame for refusing to help Eva and refers to her decision to turn her away as 'justified'.*

**a** Underline any points that link Sybil to contextual ideas about life for women in 1912.

**b** Write **one** sentence explaining your choice.

..............................................................................................................................

..............................................................................................................................

3. What other contextual ideas might be relevant for the **second** exam-style question on page 25 about Sybil Birling? Make notes below using the ideas from this page and any other ideas you might have.

..............................................................................................................................

..............................................................................................................................

..............................................................................................................................

..............................................................................................................................

..............................................................................................................................

..............................................................................................................................

## How do I include ideas about audience response?

An effective comment on the context of *An Inspector Calls* should focus on relevant beliefs and attitudes that are reflected in the play. One way to do this is to consider the impact of the play on Priestley's audience, and the way a modern audience's response might differ.

**1** Look at the beginning of one student's paragraph in response to the **second** question on page 25 (about Sybil).

**Exam-style question**

How does Priestley use the character of Sybil Birling in *An Inspector Calls* to explore ideas about responsibility?

*In Act I Sybil Birling warns Sheila that when she is married she will have to take second place as men 'spend nearly all their time and energy' on business.*

☐ **A** *This presentation of Sybil is typical of married women at the time the play was written as they were expected to stay at home even though they could vote and work. Twenty-first century women in the audience would find it difficult to sympathise with her as they expect more independence and do not feel the need to defer to men.*

☐ **B** *This acceptance of a subservient role would not have surprised Priestley's audience in 1945. Despite advances, such as women getting the vote and women taking on valuable roles in WWI, the majority of women at that time would have deferred to their husbands. To a twenty-first century audience, however, Sybil might appear to be weak and shallow as modern women expect to be independent even when married.*

☐ **C** *To an audience in 1945, Sybil would seem typical of the middle class but modern audiences would find it difficult to accept that she stayed at home and allowed her husband to take charge.*

**a** For each point below, circle Ⓐ any paragraphs that match and cross out ~~cat~~ any that don't. Two examples have already been started.

| | | | | |
|---|---|---|---|---|
| **a** | Identifies the time the play was written | A | Ⓑ | C |
| **b** | Identifies a relevant belief or attitude at that time | A | B | C |
| **c** | Considers changing beliefs and attitudes | A | B | C |
| **d** | Identifies relevant historical events or issues | A | B | ~~C~~ |
| **e** | Compares a twentieth-century audience with a twenty-first century audience | A | B | C |

**b** Which of the three paragraphs would you use when writing about Sybil Birling? Tick ✓ **one or more.**

**2** How would different audiences respond to Sybil refusing charity to Eva? Write ✎ **two** sentences explaining:

- how an audience in 1945 would feel about Eva at this point
- how beliefs and attitudes have changed since 1945
- how these changes might affect a modern audience's feelings about Sybil's actions.

..........

..........

..........

# Exploring context

To show an understanding of the context of *An Inspector Calls* you need to:

- identify the relationship between the play and its context
- use the most relevant contextual ideas in your responses
- consider the changes in audience response since the play was written.

Look again at this exam-style question from the start of the unit.

**Exam-style question**

How does Priestley use the character of Sybil Birling in *An Inspector Calls* to explore ideas about responsibility?

Write about:

- how Priestley presents Sybil
- how Priestley uses this character to explore ideas about responsibility. **(30 marks)**

**AO4 (4 marks)**

Look at these two paragraphs from one student's response.

*Priestley presents Sybil as feeling no sense of responsibility towards the lower classes. She pays no attention to her servant, Edna, unless it is to give her orders and shows no concern for her welfare as she tells her to 'wait up' until she is needed. This reflects Priestley's negative feelings about the way the rich in Edwardian society treated the working classes.*

*Sybil accepts no blame for her part in Eva's death. She is presented as very judgemental, calling Eva a girl 'of that class' and looking down on her for being single and pregnant. Despite sitting on a charitable committee, she only helps those she feels have earned it, and feels Eva 'only had herself to blame'. Beliefs about the working class had begun to change in 1945, with the introduction of the welfare state, so an audience at that time would have been more sympathetic than Sybil about Eva's situation. A twenty-first century audience would certainly feel Sybil's attitude was wrong and might even see her as cruel.*

- makes a clear point about Sybil, linking her to the theme of responsibility
- uses a key event or speech as evidence
- identifies a relevant contextual idea
- comments on audience at the time the play was written
- compares 1945 audience with modern audience response

**1** Link each point on the right to the place in the student paragraphs where it is covered and underline all the relevant words.

# Your turn!

You are now going to **write your own answer** in response to the exam-style question below.

**Exam-style question**

How does Priestley use the character of Sybil Birling in *An Inspector Calls* to explore ideas about responsibility?

Write about:

- how Priestley presents Sybil
- how Priestley uses this character to explore ideas about responsibility. **(30 marks)**

**AO4 (4 marks)**

1. Before you start your response, identify **three** key points. Expand them using the prompts below.

**Point 1:**

**Point 2:**

**Point 3:**

**Prompt 1:** Which key events can you use as evidence? Add relevant events or speeches to your points above.

**Prompt 2:** Think about any relevant contextual ideas and add them to your points above.

**Prompt 3:** Think about different audience responses. Would a modern audience respond differently from an audience at the time the play was written? How would responses reflect the attitudes and beliefs of different audiences? Add your ideas to your points above.

2. Use your planning notes to write your response to the exam-style question above on paper.

# Review your skills

## Check up

Review your response to the exam-style question on page 31. Tick the column to show how well you think you have done each of the following.

| | Not quite | Nearly there | Got it! |
|---|---|---|---|
| identified links between the play and the context | | | |
| used the most relevant contextual ideas | | | |
| commented on different audience responses to the play | | | |

Look over all of your work in this unit. Note down **three** points to remember when commenting on context in *An Inspector Calls*.

1. ..........

2. ..........

3. ..........

## Need more practice?

Here is another exam-style question for you to try.

### Exam-style question

How does Priestley explore social class in *An Inspector Calls*?

Write about:

- the ideas about social class in *An Inspector Calls*
- how Priestley presents these ideas by the ways he writes. (30 marks)

AO4 (4 marks)

Plan and write a response.

Remember to only add contextual ideas that are relevant to the point you are making.

How confident do you feel about each of these **skills?** Colour in the bars.

1. How do I make sure I know the context?
2. How do I select relevant contextual ideas?
3. How do I include ideas about audience response?

# 5 Unlocking the question

This unit will help you to understand the questions you will need to answer on *An Inspector Calls*. The skills you will build are to:

- choose the right question
- unlock the requirements of the question
- develop a critical judgement in response to the focus of the question.

In the exam you will face questions like the ones below. At the end of the unit you will write part of a response to one of these questions.

**Exam-style question**

How does Priestley explore guilt in *An Inspector Calls*?

Write about:

- the ideas about guilt in *An Inspector Calls*
- how Priestley presents these ideas by the ways he writes. **(30 marks)**

**AO4 (4 marks)**

**Exam-style question**

How does Priestley present the relationship between Sheila and Gerald in *An Inspector Calls*?

Write about:

- what Sheila and Gerald's relationship is like
- how Priestley shows their relationships by the ways he writes. **(30 marks)**

**AO4 (4 marks)**

**Before you tackle these questions, you will work through three key questions in the skills boosts to help you unlock exam questions.**

 **How do I choose a question?**

 **How do I unlock the question?**

 **How do I develop a critical judgement?**

Look at one student's notes on page 34 on the **first** exam-style question above (about guilt).

**As you read the notes, think about whether the student has:** 

- linked points to plot/setting/character and context ☐
- shown an understanding of the focus of the question ☐
- made a critical judgement in response to the focus of the question. ☐

**Exam-style question**

How does Priestley explore guilt in *An Inspector Calls*?

Write about:

- the ideas about guilt in *An Inspector Calls*
- how Priestley presents these ideas by the ways he writes. **(30 marks)**

**AO4 (4 marks)**

*Guilt – important theme as it makes characters face responsibility (Priestley's main idea in play)*

*Guilt introduced by Inspector:*

- *when bell rings they are celebrating – they joke it might be something Eric's done – typical Edwardian wealthy middle class, shows how secure they feel about social position*

*Characters used to show guilt:*

- *Arthur and Sybil show no guilt. In Act I Arthur calls his sacking of Eva 'justified' – reflects treatment of working class at time – modern audience might see this as arrogant and callous*
- *Gerald shows some guilt in Act II – wishes Eva had blamed him – 'she didn't blame me at all'; but by end of play he shows double standards – 'Everything's all right now'*
  *– reflects gender inequality of 1912 – 1945 audience would accept this*
- *Sheila and Eric show guilt – Sheila self-centred at start (feels she can never go to Milwards again) – at end says they all drove Eva to suicide – youth shown as hope for the future*

*Inspector wants each character to take responsibility:*

- *Stands for socialist ideas about responsibility – Act III key speech 'We don't live alone. We are members of one body. We are responsible for each other.' – Reflects new ideas after WWII*

1. Has the student used key events or speeches as evidence for each point? Underline one of the points where there is a clear link and label it **'evidence'**.

2. Has the student linked points to the following?

| Themes/setting | Context | Audience response | Structure |
|---|---|---|---|

Circle **one** example of each and label it **'themes'**, **'setting'**, **'context'**, **'audience'** or **'structure'**.

3. Has the student maintained a close focus on the question? Circle **Yes / No**.

## How do I choose a question?

When looking at two questions on the exam paper, it is important to choose the one you can answer most effectively. It is important *not* to choose a question just because you know a lot about a character and their part in the plot of the play. You should aim to choose a question for which you can:

- make clear points that focus on the question
- use key events or speeches as evidence
- make a link to contextual ideas.

Look at one student's initial ideas in response to both exam-style questions on page 33.

**Exam-style question**

How does Priestley explore guilt in *An Inspector Calls*?

- *Guilt important – links to responsibility*
- *Sybil and Arthur show traditional view – not guilty – felt justified*
- *Sheila and Eric represent youth – see their guilt*
- *Inspector shows importance of guilt*
- *Link to responsibility for working classes*
- *Play structured to reveal their guilt slowly*

**Exam-style question**

How does Priestley present the relationship between Sheila and Gerald in *An Inspector Calls*?

- *In love at start*
- *Sheila cross about Gerald's affair*
- *Gerald used Eva*
- *He was kind to Eva*
- *Gerald no idea what happened to Eva*
- *Sheila forgives him*
- *Gerald tries to give ring back*
- *Sheila doesn't take it*
- *Sheila says their relationship has changed*

1 Which plan makes points that focus on the question? Label it **'Points'**. The other plan uses key events to tell the story. Label it **'Plot'**.

2 One way to decide if you can write an effective response is to see whether you can link your ideas to key concepts.

a Think about the **second** question about the relationship between Sheila and Gerald. Circle (A) which of the key concepts below you could link to your response.

setting | theme | structure | context | audience

**Exam-style question**

How does Priestley present the relationship between Sheila and Gerald in *An Inspector Calls*?

Write about:

- what Sheila and Gerald's relationship is like
- how Priestley shows their relationship by the ways he writes.

b Draw lines from the key concepts to the exam-style question and annotate it to explain the links you could make.

3 You will also need to analyse the language Priestley uses. Note down **two** speeches you could link to the question about Sheila and Gerald.

**Speech 1:** ..........

**Speech 2:** ..........

## 2 How do I unlock the question?

When you have chosen a question, make sure you fully understand what it is asking. To do this, you should think carefully about:

- the words used in the question
- the links you can make to different themes and characters.

1. Some questions may use words or phrases that do not make the themes you need to focus on immediately obvious. For example, look at the themes that can be linked to this question.

**Exam-style question**

How does Priestley explore secrets and lies in *An Inspector Calls*?

*responsibility* .................... *power* ....................

a. In the spaces, write two other themes that can be linked to the idea of 'secrets and lies'.

b. List three characters who would be relevant to this question.

Character 1: .................... Character 2: .................... Character 3: ....................

2. Look at some other words and phrases that might be used in theme-based exam-style questions.

a. Link the words and phrases on the left with the major themes on the right. Some may link to more than one theme.

| | |
|---|---|
| A exploitation | a responsibility |
| B relationships | b power |
| C conflict | c equality |
| D duty | d morality |
| E hypocrisy | e love |
| F reputation | |
| G gender roles | |
| H guilty conscience | |

b. Write one or two sentences to explain one of the links you have made.

..............................

..............................

3. Now think about character-based questions. You should avoid writing everything you know about a character. Instead you should consider how the question can be linked to themes. For example:

**Exam-style question**

How does Priestley present Arthur and Sybil Birling as parents in *An Inspector Calls*?

*responsibility* .................... *power*

a. Write one other theme that could be linked to ideas about the Birlings as parents.

b. Write one sentence on paper explaining how your choice links to the question.

## How do I develop a critical judgement?

Before you plan your written response, you need to make a critical judgement on the topic in the question. To do this you need to:

- weigh up the ideas suggested in the question
- think about Priestley's intentions when he wrote the play.

① Look at this character-based exam-style question:

*How does he create conflict?*

..........

..........

..........

**Exam-style question**

How does Priestley present the Inspector as creating conflict in *An Inspector Calls*?

*Why does he create conflict?*

..........

..........

..........

*Which themes are explored through conflict?* responsibility / equality / power / morality

**a** Complete the student's ideas above.

**b** Use your notes to choose the most appropriate critical judgement. Tick your choice.

☐ **A** *In An Inspector Calls, Priestley uses the Inspector to create conflict as this forces the Birlings to think about what they did to Eva.*

☐ **B** *Priestley presents the Inspector as creating conflict as this challenges the Birlings and Gerald to think about their responsibility towards others.*

☐ **C** *The Inspector is presented as creating conflict as this helps to raise Priestley's important ideas about responsibility and morality in society.*

② Now think about how to develop a critical judgement on a theme-based exam-style question.

*Why does Priestley include the idea of power in the play?*

..........

*Does it link to other themes?*

..........

..........

..........

**Exam-style question**

How does Priestley explore the idea of power in *An Inspector Calls*?

*Which characters can be linked to power?*

..........

..........

..........

*How is power shown?* positive / negative / a bit of both

**a** Complete the student's ideas above.

**b** Use your answers to write **one** or **two** sentences summing up your critical judgement about how and why Priestley explores power in *An Inspector Calls*.

..........

..........

..........

# Unlocking the question

To write an effective response you need to show a full understanding of the focus of the question by:
- choosing the question that allows you to make clear points
- considering the words in the question and linking them to themes and characters
- developing a critical judgement that shows an understanding of Priestley's purpose.

Look again at the **second** exam-style question you saw at the start of the unit.

**Exam-style question**

How does Priestley present the relationship between Sheila and Gerald in *An Inspector Calls*?

Look at these two paragraphs from the start of one student's response to this exam-style question.

*Sheila begins the play as a rather shallow character. In the stage directions at the start, Priestley describes Sheila in terms of her physical appearance as 'a pretty girl' who is 'rather excited' about her engagement, which gives the audience an initial impression of a rather frivolous girl. Her excited reaction to the engagement also suggests she is happy to follow the traditional expectations for the daughter of a wealthy family in the early twentieth century and marry somebody who will help the family achieve a higher social status.*

*However, there are very early signs that Sheila may change. Before the Inspector's arrival she raises suspicions about Gerald's behaviour but Priestley's stage directions state that she is 'half serious, half playful', which suggests that she is still too naïve to see beyond the romance of their relationship. She is warned by her mother that men have 'important work' and wives must come second to their business interests. This is emphasised when Arthur talks about how much the engagement means to him, suggesting that to him and Gerald it is more of a business arrangement than a love match. This is the first hint in the play that love means different things to men and women.*

**1** **a** Which of these critical judgements do the paragraphs best support? Tick ✓ your choice.

☐ **A** Sheila's relationship with Gerald is important in the play as it shows how Sheila changes.

☐ **B** Priestley uses the relationship between Sheila and Gerald to explore ideas about love and responsibility.

☐ **C** In *An Inspector Calls* Sheila's relationship with Gerald shows what life was like for a traditional young lady in 1912.

**b** Underline (A) where the student has made clear points. Label them **'Points'**.

**c** Identify and label ✎ any links made to '**key themes**', '**characters**' or '**contextual ideas**'.

# Your turn!

You are now going to **write your own response** to the exam-style question below.

**Exam-style question**

How does Priestley explore guilt in *An Inspector Calls*?

Write about:

- the ideas about guilt in *An Inspector Calls*
- how Priestley presents these ideas by the ways he writes. **(30 marks)**

**AO4 (4 marks)**

1. Weigh up the ideas in the question in order to come up with a critical judgement.

   a. How is guilt shown? as positive / as negative / as a bit of both

   b. Why is it important? ..........

   c. Does it link to other themes? ..........

   ..........

   d. Why does Priestley include the idea of guilt in the play? ..........

   ..........

   ..........

   ..........

2. Note down **three** points to include in your response.

| Point 1: |
|---|
| Point 2: |
| Point 3: |

   a. Can you use key events or speeches as evidence? Add notes to your points.

   b. Can your points be linked to the following? Add notes to your ideas above.

| setting | theme | structure | context | audience | characters |
|---|---|---|---|---|---|

# Review your skills

## Check up

Review your response to the exam-style question on page 39. Tick the column to show how well you think you have done each of the following.

| | Not quite | Nearly there | Got it! |
|---|---|---|---|
| used clear points that focus on the question | | | |
| linked the response to key themes and characters | | | |
| made a critical judgement | | | |

Look over all of your work in this unit. Note down **three** points to remember when choosing a question on *An Inspector Calls*.

1. ..........
2. ..........
3. ..........

## Need more practice?

Try writing a response to the exam-style question below.

### Exam-style question

How does Priestley present the relationship between Sheila and Gerald in *An Inspector Calls*?

Write about:

- what Sheila and Gerald's relationship is like
- how Priestley shows their relationship by the ways he writes. **(30 marks)**

**AO4 (4 marks)**

Spend some time unlocking the question before you begin your planning. After you have finished your writing, check your answer. Has it covered everything the question asks for?

How confident do you feel about each of these **skills?** Colour in the bars.

# Planning your response

This unit will help you to plan your response to the exam question on *An Inspector Calls*. The skills you will build are to:

- support your critical judgement with relevant points
- use relevant evidence to support your points
- sequence your points to build a successful argument.

In the exam you will face questions like the ones below. At the end of the unit you will write your own response to one of these questions.

**Exam-style question**

How does Priestley present the Inspector as powerful during the course of the play?

Write about:

- how Priestley presents the Inspector's behaviour
- how the Inspector behaves and talks to people. **(30 marks)**

**AO4 (4 marks)**

**Exam-style question**

How does Priestley explore inequality in *An Inspector Calls*?

Write about:

- the ideas about inequality in *An Inspector Calls*
- how Priestley presents these ideas by the ways he writes. **(30 marks)**

**AO4 (4 marks)**

**Before you tackle these questions, you will work through three key questions in the skills boosts to help you plan your response.**

1 How do I make relevant points?

2 How do I select relevant evidence?

3 How do I sequence my points?

Look at one student's plan on page 42 for the **second** exam-style question above (about inequality).

**As you read the plan, think about whether the student has:**

- made relevant points that support the critical judgement ☐
- used relevant evidence that can be linked to structure, context or audience response ☐
- sequenced the points effectively to build to a conclusion. ☐

## Get started

**Exam-style question**

How does Priestley explore inequality in *An Inspector Calls*?

Write about:

- the ideas about inequality in *An Inspector Calls*
- how Priestley presents these ideas by the ways he writes. **(30 marks)**

**AO4 (4 marks)**

*Critical judgement – Priestley uses the play to comment on the lack of equality in society.*

| | |
|---|---|
| *Inequality benefits the wealthy – easy lifestyle and power* | • *Stage directions at start – contrast between Edna clearing away and 'comfortable' dining room setting*<br>• *Birlings in evening dress*<br>• *Arthur boasts about expecting a knighthood* |
| *Eva used to represent effect of inequality on w/classes – wealthy able to exploit* | • *Easily fired from jobs in factory and shop*<br>• *Dependent on men – Gerald and Eric*<br>• *Lack of opportunities shown by Arthur's question – 'Get into trouble? Go on the streets?' (Act I)*<br>*Shows inequality before welfare state and also the gender inequality of the time* |
| *Inspector challenges and suggests new way* | • *Argues with Arthur about Eva's sacking*<br>• *Criticises factories that exploit w/classes*<br>• *Says 'We are responsible for each other' (Act III)*<br>*Reflects Priestley's views about social responsibility – widely accepted today, but intended to educate original audience* |

*Conclusion – Sheila and Eric represent hope for more equality in future*

1. The student has made points that support their critical judgement. Highlight and label the student's notes to show where the evidence they use to support their points will allow them to comment on '**structure**', '**context**' and '**audience response**'.

2. How does the conclusion about Sheila and Eric link to the student's critical judgement? Write **one** or **two** sentences explaining the link.

..............................................................................................................................................

..............................................................................................................................................

..............................................................................................................................................

# How do I make relevant points?

You will need to make a range of points to support your critical judgement. It is important to focus on the words in the question, rather than just telling the story of the play or the characters.

1. Look again at the exam-style questions on page 41. Your points should address the word 'how' in the question. These points are about the presentation of the Inspector.

| Presentation of the Inspector | ✓ | ✗ |
|---|---|---|
| He is not intimidated by the Birlings. | | |
| He represents Priestley's ideas about responsibility. | | |
| He challenges the Birlings and Gerald. | | |
| He isn't a real Inspector. | | |
| His visit turns out to be a hoax. | | |
| Edna shows him in. | | |
| He exposes the family's lack of morals. | | |

a. Tick ✓ the **four** most relevant points.

b. Put a cross ✗ next to any points you think are just telling the story.

2. You can also use the bullet points in the questions to help you make relevant points. For example, look at the **second** exam-style question from page 41 about inequality.

**Exam-style question**

How does Priestley explore inequality in *An Inspector Calls*?

Write about:

- the ideas about inequality in *An Inspector Calls*

Look at one student's points for this question.

*Eva's life is difficult.* ☐

*Inequality allows wealthy to exploit working class.* ☐

*The Birlings are wealthy.* ☐

*Gerald is superior to the Birlings.* ☐

*working class have fewer opportunities.* ☐

*The Birlings benefit from inequality.* ☐

Which points cover 'ideas about inequality'? Tick ✓ them, then cross ✗ any ideas that simply tell the story of the play or characters.

# 2 How do I select relevant evidence?

You will need to support each of your points with relevant evidence. Evidence should be a specific event or speech from *An Inspector Calls* rather than a general statement, and you should cover the whole of the play. Evidence should also allow you to make links to structure, context and audience response.

Look again at the **first** exam-style question from page 41. Then look at points **1**, **2** and **3** below about how the Inspector is powerful.

**Exam-style question**

How does Priestley present the Inspector as powerful during the course of the play?

| Point | Relevant evidence | Structure, context or audience response |
|---|---|---|
| **Point 1:** He exposes the Birlings' lack of compassion for others. | | |
| **Point 2:** He is not intimidated by the Birlings' superior class. | | |
| **Point 3:** His power shows the importance of his message about responsibility. | | |

① a Now look at some of the Inspector's key moments and speeches from the play. Note the most relevant as evidence for each of the points in the table above.

- **A** (Act I) He arrives as Arthur is talking about men being responsible for themselves.
- **B** (Act I) Soon after arriving, he interrupts Arthur – '*cutting through, massively*'.
- **C** (Act I) He refuses to let Gerald and Eric look at the photograph.
- **D** (Act III) He gives a final warning that if people don't take responsibility for others they will pay with 'fire and blood and anguish'.
- **E** (Act II) Mrs Birling refuses to take any blame for turning Eva away.
- **F** (Act I) He insists Gerald stays and listens to the questioning of Arthur.

b For **one** of the points, write **one** sentence explaining why the evidence you have chosen supports the point.

..........

..........

② Think about how your evidence could be used to comment on **structure**, **context** or **audience response**. Write **S**, **C** or **AR** next to each of the points above to show where a relevant comment could be made. Then select **two** of the points and write **one** or **two** sentences explaining the link.

Point number ..........

..........

Point number ..........

..........

## 3 How do I sequence my points?

You need to sequence your points to build a logical argument that supports your critical judgement. The easiest way to do this is to take a chronological approach. However, you can also link your points by character, theme or author's approach.

Look at this exam-style question and one student's critical judgement in response to it.

**Exam-style question**

How does Priestley explore inequality in *An Inspector Calls*?

*Priestley uses An Inspector Calls to explore his ideas about inequality in society.*

Now look at these four key points, taken from the same student's plan.

A ☐ *Inequality shown through Eva's lack of opportunities.*

B ☐ *Inequality benefits wealthy like the Birlings and Gerald.*

C ☐ *Gender inequality shown through the way men use Eva.*

D ☐ *Inspector points out how society could be more equal.*

**chronological**: in time order

① One way to sequence the key points in a response is to work your way through the play **chronologically**: exploring how a character or theme develops as the play progresses.
How would you sequence key points (**A–D**) above if you were organising a response **chronologically**? Number the points in the boxes above.

**synthesise**: combine or group together

② Another way to organise key points in a response is to **synthesise** them: grouping related points together – for example, about a character or the author's approach.

a Write **one** sentence about how you would sequence key points **A–D** above if you were exploring how Priestley shows inequality first through one character, then through another.

..........

..........

b Write **one** sentence about how you would sequence key points **A–D** above if you were looking at one way in which Priestley explores inequality, then another way in which he explores inequality, and so on.

..........

..........

③ a Tick the method you would choose to sequence key points **A–D** above:

☐ Chronologically

☐ Synthesising key points about the author's approach

☐ Synthesising key points about character

b Write **one** or **two** sentences explaining your choice on paper.

# Planning your response

To plan an effective response you need to:

- make relevant points that support your critical judgement
- support each of your points with relevant evidence that can be linked to structure, context and audience response
- sequence your points – decide on the most effective way to build a logical argument that supports your critical judgement (for example, chronologically, by character or by approach).

Look again at the **first** exam-style question you saw at the start of the unit.

**Exam-style question**

How does Priestley present the Inspector as powerful during the course of the play?

Write about:

- how Priestley presents the Inspector's behaviour
- how the Inspector behaves and talks to people. **(30 marks)**

**AO4 (4 marks)**

Look at these two paragraphs, written by a student in response to the exam-style question above.

*The Inspector is presented as powerful as he is used by Priestley to present his ideas about the need for an equal and just society.*

*Priestley first suggests he is powerful as the stage directions describe him as creating an impression of 'massiveness, solidity and purposefulness', who looks hard at the people he addresses before speaking. This suggests he will be an imposing and dominating figure who will achieve his aims. The lighting changes when he arrives and becomes 'brighter and harder', which symbolises his power and the fact that he will reveal the family's secrets. This would encourage an audience to see the Inspector as an important character and to listen carefully to what he has to say.*

*In Act I he appears powerful as he refuses to be intimidated by the Birlings' superior social status. He is not impressed by Arthur's claims to know the local police and interrupts him by 'cutting in, massively'. He also insists Gerald stays during the questioning of Arthur, despite Arthur's boasting that Gerald is from the upper classes. This powerful approach from a policeman might have surprised an audience in 1945, as wealthy families were used to commanding respect at that time. However, a modern audience would think it right that wealth does not put you above the law.*

1. Underline (A) where the student has supported the two points about the Inspector with relevant and specific evidence. Label it '**evidence**'.

2. Highlight where the student has made links to structure, context and audience response. Label them '**structure**', '**context**' or '**audience response**'.

3. Tick how this student has organised their key points.

   A chronologically ☐ B by character ☐ C by approach ☐

# Your turn!

You are now going to **write your own response** to the exam-style question below.

**Exam-style question**

How does Priestley present the Inspector as powerful during the course of the play?

Write about:

- how Priestley presents the Inspector's behaviour
- how the Inspector behaves and talks to people. **(30 marks)**

**AO4 (4 marks)**

1 Note below the key points you will make in your response. Remember to consider the words in the question and make a range of points that cover the whole play.

| Point 1: |
| --- |
| Point 2: |
| Point 3: |
| Point 4: |

2 Which specific **events** or **speeches** in the play will you use as evidence for your points? Add them to your plan above.

3 Which of your points can be linked to the ideas below? Note this on your plan.

structure | context | audience response

4 a How will you sequence your key points? Tick **one** answer.

☐ chronologically ☐ by character ☐ by approach

b Note the order of your key points so that you sequence them to build an argument that supports your critical judgement.

*The order of my key points will be:* .................. .................. .................. ..................

5 Now write your response to the exam-style question above on paper.

# Review your skills

## Check up

Review your response to the exam-style question on page 47. Tick the column to show how well you think you have done each of the following.

| | Not quite | Nearly there | Got it! |
|---|---|---|---|
| made key points using key words from the question | ☐ | ☐ | ☐ |
| used relevant evidence that can be linked to structure, context and audience | ☐ | ☐ | ☐ |
| sequenced my key points to build an argument that supports my critical judgement | ☐ | ☐ | ☐ |

Look over all of your work in this unit. Note down **three** points to remember when planning a response.

1. ..............................
2. ..............................
3. ..............................

## Need more practice?

Try writing a response to the exam-style question below.

### Exam-style question

How does Priestley explore inequality in *An Inspector Calls*?

Write about:

- the ideas about inequality in *An Inspector Calls*
- how Priestley presents these ideas by the ways he writes. **(30 marks)**

**AO4 (4 marks)**

Remember to start by underlining key words in the question.

How confident do you feel about each of these **skills?** Colour in the bars.

1. How do I make relevant points?
2. How do I select relevant evidence?
3. How do I sequence my points?

Get started

**Analyse the language, form and structure used by a writer to create meanings and effects (AO2)**

# Writer's methods

This unit will help you to comment on Priestley's writing methods in *An Inspector Calls*. The skills you will build are to:

- identify relevant language choices to comment on
- identify relevant form and structural choices to comment on
- make effective comments on the writer's choices.

In the exam you will face questions like the ones below. At the end of the unit you will write your own response to one of these questions.

**Exam-style question**

How does Priestley present the relationship between parents and children in *An Inspector Calls*?

Write about:

- how Priestley presents the relationship between parents and children
- how Priestley uses the relationship to explore some of his ideas. **(30 marks)**

**AO4 (4 marks)**

**Exam-style question**

How does Priestley present learning from experience in *An Inspector Calls*?

Write about:

- the ways particular characters learn from experience throughout the play
- how Priestley presents learning from experience by the ways he writes. **(30 marks)**

**AO4 (4 marks)**

**Before you tackle these questions, you will work through three key questions in the skills boosts to help you comment on the writer's methods.**

1. How do I identify significant language choices?
2. How do I identify significant form and structural choices?
3. How do I comment on the writer's choices?

Look at the extract from one student's response on page 50 to the **second** exam-style question above (about learning from experience).

**As you read the extract, think about whether the student has:** ✓

| identified the most relevant language choices to support the points made ☐ | identified the most relevant form and structural choices to support the points made ☐ | commented on the effect of the language and structure. ☐ |
|---|---|---|

## Get started

**Exam-style question**

How does Priestley present learning from experience in *An Inspector Calls*?

Write about:

- the ways particular characters learn from experience throughout the play
- how Priestley presents learning from experience by the ways he writes. **(30 marks)**

**AO4 (4 marks)**

*At the start of the play, before the Inspector arrives, Arthur Birling is presented as the voice of experience. He is shown to dominate the play at this point as he is given the most lines and has several very long speeches. He boasts of having learned from experience at the 'hard school of business' and lectures the younger members of the family, saying 'Now you three young people, just listen to this –'. The use of the imperative 'listen' after the word 'Now' shows he feels in charge. This would be emphasised on stage by the dramatic pause before he starts his speech, which would suggest to the audience that he is about to say something important.*

*However, as the play progresses it becomes clear that the elder Birlings have not learned from their experience with the Inspector. Once the visit is revealed to be a hoax, Arthur dismisses his worries and relaxes, pouring drinks and speaking 'jovially'. When he imitates the Inspector, and says 'You all helped to kill her' the audience will see that he has learned nothing, and feel disgusted at his callous jokes about a young girl's death. This reflects Priestley's views that the rich in society are self-interested and take no responsibility for the rest of society.*

1. Underline and label where the student has:
   - used a specific quotation – label as **'quotation'**
   - commented on audience response – label as **'audience'**
   - commented on the effect of specific language choices – label as **'language'**
   - commented on stage directions – label as **'stage directions'**.

2. At what other specific points in the play does Arthur Birling show he has learned nothing from the Inspector? Write down **two** key events.

   Key event 1: ..............................................................

   ..............................................................

   Key event 2: ..............................................................

   ..............................................................

## How do I identify significant language choices?

To identify significant language choices, think about the way Priestley uses dialogue to:

- reflect the characters' distinct personalities
- show their attitudes towards his key ideas.

You will then need to identify a key speech to use in your response. Remember to keep your quotations short by focusing on key words and phrases rather than using whole speeches.

Each character's speech reflects their personality. For example, Arthur Birling is domineering and self-important. He frequently interrupts others to put forward his views.

1 Look at this dialogue.

Act I

**Eric:** Yes, I know – but still—

**Birling:** Just let me finish, Eric. You've a lot to learn yet. And I'm talking as a hard-headed, practical man of business. And I say there isn't a chance of war.

a Which words or short phrases best suggest Birling is domineering? Circle (A) your choices.

b Which words or short phrases suggest Birling is self-important? Underline (A) your choices.

2 Look at another exchange of dialogue, this time between Eric and his mother.

Act III

**Eric:** (*nearly at breaking point*) Then – you killed her. She came to you to protect me – and you turned her away – yes, and you killed her – and the child she'd have had too – my child – your own grandchild – you killed them both – damn you, damn you—

**Mrs Birling:** (*very distressed now*) No – Eric – please – I didn't know – I didn't understand—

a Underline (A) any words or short phrases that suggest Eric is hot-headed.

b What does Priestley's choice of words or phrases suggest about the relationship between Eric and his mother at this point in the play? Highlight (✎) **two** words or phrases and annotate (✎) them with your ideas.

3 Some speeches are significant because they relate to several themes in the play. Look at these exam-style questions and a speech from Act III.

**Exam-style question**

How does Priestley present the relationship between parents and children in *An Inspector Calls*?

**Exam-style question**

How does Priestley present learning from experience in *An Inspector Calls*?

Act III

**Birling:** Well, my dear, they're so damned exasperating. They just won't try to understand our position or to see the difference between a lot of stuff like this coming out in private and a downright public scandal.

a Identify and underline (A) **two** short phrases from Birling's speech that link to the first question (about family relationships).

b Circle (A) **two** short phrases from Birling's speech that link to the **second** question (about learning from experience).

## How do I identify significant form and structural choices?

When you think about Priestley's form and structural choices, you need to remember that *An Inspector Calls* is a play. This means you must consider the effect of the play's form and structure on the audience's appreciation of the play.

Look at this extract from *An Inspector Calls*.

Act II

**Birling:** (*terrified now*) Look Inspector, you're not trying to tell us that – that my boy – is mixed up in this—?

**Inspector:** (*sternly*) If he is, then we know what to do, don't we? Mrs Birling has just told us.

**Birling:** (*thunderstruck*) My God! But – look here—

**Mrs Birling:** (*agitated*) I don't believe it. I *won't* believe it …

**Sheila:** Mother – I begged you and begged you to stop—

Inspector *holds up a hand. We hear the front door. They wait, looking towards door. Eric enters, looking extremely pale and distressed. He meets their inquiring stares. Curtain falls quickly.*

One way to think about the form (or genre) of *An Inspector Calls* is to consider how it works as a 'whodunnit'. Throughout the play, the audience would be trying to work out who was responsible for the death of Eva Smith.

**1** Act II ends on a 'cliff-hanger'. What mood will this create for the audience? Tick ✓ your choice.

serious ☐ anxious ☐ tense ☐ frightening ☐ exciting ☐

**2** Another relevant genre is the 'morality' play, where the audience are invited to judge the characters' actions.

How would an audience judge Mrs Birling at this point in the play? Tick ✓ your choice.

A They would be shocked by her lack of knowledge about her son. ☐

B They would be sympathetic as she is worried about her son. ☐

C They would feel satisfied as she deserves to be punished. ☐

D They would hate her for what she did to Eva. ☐

**3** Now look at the stage directions in the extract above. Think about how they are used to present Mr and Mrs Birling as unsatisfactory parents. Highlight **two** stage directions that suggest Mr and Mrs Birling are out of touch with their children's lives. Try to keep your selections short.

**4** Think about the overall structure of the play. Why does Priestley keep Eric off stage until this point? Write **one** or **two** sentences explaining your ideas.

..........

..........

..........

## How do I comment on the writer's choices?

An effective comment on the writer's choice of language, form and structure will highlight the choice the writer has made and comment on its *effect*.

Read this extract along with some of the different comments you could make about its language, form and structure.

Act III

**Eric:** Yes. And that's when it happened. And I didn't even remember – that's the hellish thing. Oh – my God! – how stupid it all is!

**Mrs Birling:** (*with a cry*) Oh – Eric – how could you?

**Birling:** (*sharply*) Sheila, take your mother along to the drawing-room—

**Sheila:** (*protesting*) But – I want to—

**Birling:** (*very sharply*) You heard what I said. (*Gentler.*) Go on, Sybil.

The dialogue is realistic, so there is less emphasis on imagery and more on plain, and at times emotive, language.

**Choice**

- A emotive language: 'how stupid it all is!'
- B the adverb 'even'
- C religious language: 'hellish' and 'Oh – my God!'
- D '(protesting)'
- E 'Oh – my God!'
- F 'Oh – Eric – how could you?'

**Effect**

- a suggests Sheila is losing respect for her father as she dares to challenge him
- b emphasises Eric's guilt at his drunken behaviour
- c suggests Eric's distress
- d dramatic pauses emphasise his distress and suggest he is starting to blame himself
- e characters start to blame each other, which makes audience consider their own feelings about what has happened
- f suggests ideas about sin and confession

1. Draw lines to link Priestley's language, form and structure choices to the effect they have.

Choices **A-C** comment on language, choices **D-F** on form and structure.

2. Underline any other interesting language, form and/or structure choices. Write **one** or **two** sentences explaining their effect.

Think about how stage directions and language are used to show a difference in Arthur Birling's feelings about Sheila and Sybil.

......................................................................

......................................................................

......................................................................

# Writer's methods

To comment effectively on Priestley's choice of language, form and structure, you need to:
- use short quotations that reflect character or theme
- consider how the form and structure choices affect audience appreciation of the play
- highlight the specific choices Priestley has made and comment on their effect.

Look again at the **first** exam-style question you saw at the start of the unit:

**Exam-style question**

How does Priestley present the relationship between parents and children in *An Inspector Calls*?

Write about:
- how Priestley presents the relationship between parents and children
- how Priestley uses the relationship to explore some of his ideas. **(30 marks)**

**AO4 (4 marks)**

Read this paragraph taken from one student's response to the question.

**Key features of an effective paragraph of analysis**

key point focusing on the key words in the question

short quotations as evidence

stage directions used as evidence

some link to the context of the play

*At the end of the play Priestley uses the relationship between Arthur and Eric to show how little the older generation has learned about morals and responsibility. After the Inspector has left, the relationship between parents and children falls apart. Eric openly challenges Arthur's authority by 'shouting' when he tells him that they all killed Eva. The tension is escalated as Arthur also shouts, but is 'threatening', which suggests he feels he has lost control of his relationship with his son. His use of the imperative idiom 'hold your tongue' creates a very aggressive image and shows how angry he is that the traditional expectation of respect for the older generation is being ignored. This aggression would cause the audience to be openly judgemental about Arthur as it shows he has learned nothing from the experience with the Inspector; he is still more concerned about himself.*

**Key features of an effective comment on the writer's choices**

some reference to the specific type of language or language features used

a comment on the effect of language choice(s)

a comment on the effect of structural choice(s)

a comment on the audience's reaction to the form of the play

1. Look at the annotations around the student's answer. Use lines and circles to link each annotation to part of the student's answer.

# Your turn!

You are now going to **write your own response** to the exam-style question below.

**Exam-style question**

How does Priestley present the relationship between parents and children in *An Inspector Calls*?

Write about:

- how Priestley presents the relationship between parents and children
- how Priestley uses the relationship to explore some of his ideas. **(30 marks)**

**AO4 (4 marks)**

1 Write **one** sentence giving your critical judgement in response to the exam-style question.

..........

..........

2 List below the key points you will make in your response. Remember to consider the words in the question and make a range of points that cover the whole play.

Point 1:

Point 2:

Point 3:

Point 4:

3 Now add examples of the following to support your points:

a short words or phrases you can use as quotations to comment on Priestley's language choices

b stage directions to show structure

c a link to the 'whodunnit' or morality form of the play

4 Add a relevant contextual idea to **one** of your points.

5 Now write your response on paper.

Think about the play as a performance – don't forget to consider the audience.

# Review your skills

## Check up

Review your response to the exam-style question on page 55. Tick the column to show how well you think you have done each of the following:

| | Not quite | Nearly there | Got it! |
|---|---|---|---|
| structured an effective paragraph of analysis in response to the question | ☐ | ☐ | ☐ |
| commented on Priestley's language choices | ☐ | ☐ | ☐ |
| commented on Priestley's choices of form and structure | ☐ | ☐ | ☐ |

Look over all of your work in this unit. Note down **three** points to remember when commenting on a writer's methods.

1. ..........
2. ..........
3. ..........

## Need more practice?

Try writing a response to the exam-style question below.

### Exam-style question

How does Priestley present learning from experience in *An Inspector Calls*?

Write about:

- the ways particular characters learn from experience throughout the play
- how Priestley presents learning from experience by the ways he writes. **(30 marks)**

**AO4 (4 marks)**

Think about:

- how Priestley uses language to show character
- specific types of language or language features used
- connotations of individual words or phrases.

How confident do you feel about each of these **skills?** Colour in the bars.

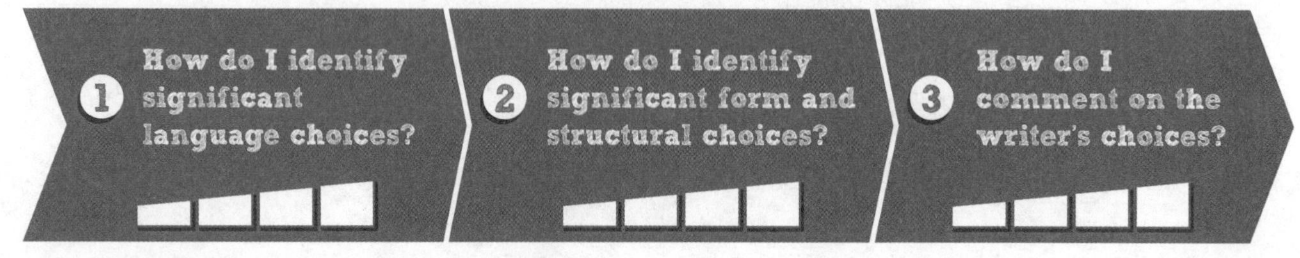

# 8 Writing a response

This unit will help you to develop your points in your response. The skills you will build are to:

- use quotations and paraphrasing as evidence
- link analysis and interpretation to context and audience
- develop your points.

In the exam you will face questions like the ones below. At the end of this unit you will write your own response to one of these questions.

**Exam-style question**

How does Priestley use the character of Eva Smith in *An Inspector Calls* to explore ideas about exploitation?

Write about:

- how Priestley presents Eva Smith
- how Priestley uses this character to explore ideas about exploitation. **(30 marks)**

**AO4 (4 marks)**

**Exam-style question**

How does Priestley present age in *An Inspector Calls*?

Write about:

- the ideas about age in *An Inspector Calls*
- how Priestley presents these ideas by the ways he writes. **(30 marks)**

**AO4 (4 marks)**

**Before you tackle these questions, you will work through three key questions in the skills boosts to help you write your response.**

1. How do I use quotations in my response?
2. How do I link my analysis to context?
3. How do I develop my points?

Look at two paragraphs from one student's response on page 58 to the **first** exam-style question above (about Eva Smith).

**As you read the paragraphs, think about:** ✓

- how the student has used evidence ☐
- how the student has linked analysis to contextual ideas ☐
- how the student has developed each point. ☐

**Exam-style question**

How does Priestley use the character of Eva Smith in *An Inspector Calls* to explore ideas about exploitation?

Write about:

- how Priestley presents Eva Smith
- how Priestley uses this character to explore ideas about exploitation. **(30 marks)**

**AO4 (4 marks)**

*Eva Smith is used by Priestley to represent the working classes and show how easily they were exploited by the wealthy. For example, she is not seen on stage, she is only described by others. This is important as it shows how wealthy families like the Birlings rely on the working classes without ever really seeing them as real people. This reflects the gap between the upper and lower classes in Edwardian society.*

- link between explanation and context
- a point that links to the question
- explanation of evidence
- evidence about how a character is presented

*Eva Smith is first presented to the audience through Arthur Birling in a positive way. This is shown when Arthur praises her, calling her a 'lively good-looking girl' and a 'good worker'. This suggests he thought she was a good employee. This was not unusual, as many factories liked employing women in 1912 as women could be paid less and were not under the protection of trade unions. This meant that if the women protested about their low pay, they could easily be sacked. This is shown in the play when Arthur talks of Eva being sacked for having 'a lot to say – far too much'. He also describes her as one of the 'ring-leaders'. This shows his distrust of the working classes as it has connotations of illegality or criminal activity.*

- extra detail
- a clear point
- analysis of language in extra detail
- link between explanation and context
- how context is shown in play
- evidence
- explanation of effect

(1) Read both paragraphs above. Then draw lines linking each comment to the relevant part of its paragraph. Underline all the words in the paragraph that apply to each comment.

## How do I use quotations in my response?

When you write your response, you will need to present your evidence effectively. You can use quotations or paraphrasing to do this.

Look at how one student has used quotations in a response.

*Arthur is shown to have no respect for the working classes. This is shown when he uses the adverb 'sharply' to describe how strikers should be handled, which suggests that the working classes deserve to be treated very harshly. Gerald then immediately agrees with Arthur, suggesting it was a commonly held view at the time: 'I should say so!'*

When analysing individual words or language features it is best to keep quotations short and embed them within your explanations.

When you are not embedding a quotation into a sentence you should introduce it with a colon.

*At the start of the play Arthur, as the older generation, is presented as dominant. For example, he is given the longest speeches, he interrupts others to put forward his point of view and he boasts of his business experience. This all reflects his position as head of the family.*

If you do not need to explain the effect of language or language features, or if you are writing about structural features, you can paraphrase key events before interpreting their meaning.

**1** Look at this extract from one of Arthur's speeches.

**Act I**

But the way some of these cranks talk and write now, you'd think everybody has to look after everybody else, as if we were all mixed up together like bees in a hive – community and all that nonsense. But take my word for it, you youngsters – and I've learnt in the good hard school of experience – that a man has to mind his own business and look after himself and his own – and—

*(We hear the sharp ring of a door bell. Birling stops to listen.)*

**a** Write **one** or **two** sentences analysing how Priestley uses language to present Arthur's views about society. Use **one** of the underlined words or phrases as an embedded quotation.

..........

..........

**b** How does this speech show that Arthur Birling feels his experience is valuable? Write **one** explanatory sentence using quotations or paraphrasing the speech.

..........

..........

**c** The arrival of the Inspector interrupts this speech. Why is it important that he arrives at this point? Write **one** or **two** sentences using paraphrasing or quotations to support your ideas.

..........

..........

##  How do I link my analysis to context?

When you write about context or audience it is important that your ideas flow smoothly from your explanations rather than standing alone as a general comment.

Look again at the exam-style question about exploitation. Then read an extract from one student's response and ideas **A**, **B** and **C**.

**Exam-style question**

How does Priestley use the character of Eva Smith in *An Inspector Calls* to explore ideas about exploitation?

*Sheila is also shown as capable of exploiting Eva through her social status. This is shown by her petty jealousy over Eva who she causes to be sacked just for being 'impertinent' when Sheila is trying on a dress. The use of the adjective 'impertinent' suggests Sheila felt superior to Eva, and would therefore have felt justified in getting her dismissed.*

**A** This reflects the fact that it would have been easy for a girl like Eva to be sacked in 1912, as there was little employment protection and very few trade unions.

**B** A modern audience would not agree with this treatment of Eva.

**C** In 1912 society was very divided and the upper classes felt they were a long way above the working classes.

1. Which of these three ideas (**A**, **B** or **C**) do you feel best links with the highlighted text?  ..........

2. Read another extract from the student's response. Then add comments on **context** and **audience response** to the plan below.

*Gerald and Eric are both shown to have abused their power over Eva.*
*For example, Eric talks about being in 'that state when a chap easily turns nasty' on the night he went home with Eva.*
*His suggestion that he could have turned 'nasty' suggests he had no choice but to exploit Eva.*
*Talking about himself in the third person also makes it seem as if this is acceptable and commonplace behaviour.*

| Contextual comment | Audience comment |
|---|---|
| .................... | .................... |
| .................... | .................... |
| .................... | .................... |
| .................... | .................... |
| .................... | .................... |
| .................... | .................... |

## How do I develop my points?

A good response will develop each point in detail. To do this you can:

- add further evidence to support your point
- develop your analysis with additional interpretations.

A developed response will use more than one piece of evidence to support each point. For example:

Three different pieces of evidence are used to support the point.

One of the quotations is analysed fully to explain the effect.

*Arthur is shown to be out of touch with the world around him: he talks about the danger of labour trouble having passed, he dismisses any chance of war and he talks about the Titanic being 'absolutely unsinkable'. His language is very confident here with his use of the adverb 'absolutely' suggesting that nobody can argue with his views.*

**1** **a** Add a second piece of evidence to develop this student's answer.

*(**Point**) When the Inspector arrives, the younger generation starts to challenge traditional age roles.*
*(**Evidence**) This is first shown when Eric criticises his father for sacking Eva and then* ..................................

..................................................................................................

**b** Comment on the effect of the evidence.

..................................................................................................

..................................................................................................

Another way to develop your points is to think about additional interpretations.

**2** Underline the first interpretation below and circle the additional interpretation.

*Arthur shows he feels justified in exploiting the working classes. This is shown when he says it is his 'duty' to keep 'labour costs' down. The use of the phrase 'labour costs' suggests that he sees his employees as just a resource to be used. The word 'costs' also suggests his annoyance at having to pay them.*

**3** Complete the first interpretation in this student's answer, then write an additional interpretation about the death of Eva.

Think about the connotations of 'disinfectant'. What is it used for?

*Eva's death is used to show how damaging exploitation could be. For example, the Inspector refers to her having swallowed a lot of 'strong disinfectant' which 'burnt her inside out'. This creates a horrible image and suggests Eva must have been* ..................................

.................................................................................................. .

*It also* ..................................................................................................

.................................................................................................. .

# Writing a response

To write an effective response you need to:

- think about how you present your evidence
- make sure your context flows clearly from your points
- develop your points with extra evidence or additional interpretations.

Look again at the **second** exam-style question you saw at the start of the unit.

**Exam-style question**

How does Priestley present age in *An Inspector Calls*?

Write about:

- the ideas about age in *An Inspector Calls*
- how Priestley presents these ideas by the ways he writes.

Read this paragraph, taken from one student's response to this question.

> *Traditional ideas about age are presented at the start of the play. For instance, Sheila is presented as rather childish as she still refers to her parents as 'Mummy' and 'Daddy' despite being engaged to Gerald. She is also still treated as a child by her mother, who answers 'Of course she does' when she doesn't reply to Gerald. The use of the phrase 'of course' also shows that her mother expects Sheila to do what she is told. This reflects the traditional view that young people should respect and obey their elders, and this would have been even more expected at the time the play was set.*
>
> *Eric is also presented as rather childish at the start of the play. For example, he 'suddenly guffaws' for no reason and appears to be drunk. His behaviour is obviously unacceptable to the Birling parents as they 'look at him' and even Sheila talks to him 'severely'. The use of the word 'guffaws' suggests uncontrollable laughter, which presents him as irresponsible as well as childish. It also hints that he might be an unpredictable character later in the play. Later in the play Eric begins to challenge his parents more openly ...*

1. a. Underline where the student has used more than one piece of evidence to support a point. Label as **'evidence'**.

   b. Circle where the student has embedded quotations into their sentences. Label as **'embedded quotations'**.

   c. Highlight where the student has developed the response with additional interpretations. Label as **'additional interpretations'**.

   d. Tick where the student has used context that flows clearly from the point. Label as **'Flows clearly'**.

2. What evidence would you use for the final point about Eric? Write **one** or **two** sentences on paper including evidence as embedded quotations. Try to include more than one quotation.

# Your turn!

You are now going to **write a response** to the exam-style question below.

**Exam-style question**

How does Priestley use the character of Eva Smith in *An Inspector Calls* to explore ideas about exploitation?

Write about:

- how Priestley presents Eva Smith
- how Priestley uses this character to explore ideas about exploitation. **(30 marks)**

**AO4 (4 marks)**

1. How do you think Priestley presents Eva Smith? What ideas about exploitation does he explore? Write **one** sentence giving your critical judgement in response to the question.

2. Note below the key points you will make in your response.

Remember to consider the words in the question and make a range of points that cover the whole play.

Point 1:

Point 2:

Point 3:

Point 4:

3. Add the following to support your points:
   a. short quotations you can embed in your sentences and use to analyse Priestley's language choices
   b. links to contextual ideas and audience responses

4. Look carefully at your plan. Is there anywhere you could develop your points by adding more evidence? Are there any opportunities to add additional interpretations?

5. Now write your response on paper.

# Review your skills

## Check up

Review your response to the exam-style question on page 63. Tick the column to show how well you think you have done each of the following:

| | Not quite | Nearly there | Got it! |
|---|---|---|---|
| used quotations correctly | ☐ | ☐ | ☐ |
| linked contextual or audience ideas smoothly | ☐ | ☐ | ☐ |
| developed your points | ☐ | ☐ | ☐ |

Look over all of your work in this unit. Note down **three** points to remember when writing a response.

1. ..........

2. ..........

3. ..........

## Need more practice?

Try writing a response to the exam-style question below.

### Exam-style question

How does Priestley present age in *An Inspector Calls*?

Write about:

- the ideas about age in *An Inspector Calls*
- how Priestley presents these ideas by the ways he writes.

(30 marks)

AO4 (4 marks)

Remember to start your response with a critical judgment that sums up your ideas.

How confident do you feel about each of these **skills?** Colour in the bars.

1. How do I use quotations in my response?
2. How do I link my analysis to context?
3. How do I develop my points?

# 9 Developing a critical writing style

This unit will help you to express your ideas about *An Inspector Calls* as clearly and precisely as possible. The skills you will build are to:

- select vocabulary to expand your ideas and express them precisely
- link your ideas to express them clearly
- extend your sentences to develop your ideas more fully.

In the exam you will face questions like the ones below. At the end of the unit you will write a paragraph in response to one of these questions.

**Exam-style question**

How does Priestley explore love in *An Inspector Calls*?

Write about:

- the ideas about love in *An Inspector Calls*
- how Priestley presents these ideas by the ways he writes. **(30 marks)**

**AO4 (4 marks)**

**Exam-style question**

How does Priestley use the Inspector in *An Inspector Calls* to explore ideas about a fair society?

Write about:

- how Priestley presents the Inspector
- how Priestley uses the Inspector to explore ideas about a fair society. **(30 marks)**

**AO4 (4 marks)**

**Before you tackle these questions, you will work through three key questions in the skills boosts to help you plan your response.**

1. **How do I choose precise vocabulary?**
2. **How do I link my ideas to express them more clearly?**
3. **How do I extend my sentences to develop my ideas more fully?**

Look at an extract from one student's response on page 66 to the **first** exam-style question above (about love).

**As you read the extract, think about whether the student has:** 

- used a range of ambitious and precise vocabulary ☐
- linked sentences so that ideas are expressed clearly ☐
- used a range of sentence styles to develop ideas fully. ☐

**Exam-style question**

How does Priestley explore love in *An Inspector Calls*?

Write about:

- the ideas about love in *An Inspector Calls*
- how Priestley presents these ideas by the ways he writes. **(30 marks)**

**AO4 (4 marks)**

*Priestley uses the theme of love in An Inspector Calls to explore ideas about the different values of men and women.*

*When the play opens, love is presented in a positive way. For example, the family are celebrating Sheila and Gerald's engagement and the stage directions say they are 'pleased with themselves'. Also, during the toast to the couple, Sheila and Gerald 'look at each other'. At this time Sheila is 'quiet and serious'. This suggests they are deeply committed to each other whilst also reflecting a romantic view of love that audiences would find easy to relate to and understand.*

*However, there are suggestions of unease about the relationship in Sheila's behaviour. For example, her first speech is directed to be spoken 'gaily'. It is also supposed to be said 'possessively'. This has connotations of a clingy and demanding character. This jealous side to her character is also hinted at by her reaction to the ring, 'Now I really feel engaged', which encourages an audience to feel that she had some doubts about Gerald's commitment before that night.*

*Gerald also shows signs of uncertainty. When he responds to the toast he uses the verbs 'hope' and 'deserve', suggesting he has some qualms about the relationship. He also uses the verbs 'insist' and 'trying' when talking about being part of the family, repeating the phrase 'Haven't I?' when Sheila fails to answer. This might all suggest to an audience that both Gerald and Sheila have had some reservations about their relationship.*

1. Circle **three** examples of ambitious vocabulary. Label them **'ambitious'**.
2. Underline **three** examples of conjunctions used to link sentences. Label them **'conjunctions'**.
3. Highlight any sentences you feel could be linked to create a more critical style. Label them **'critical style'**.
4. What other ideas about love are present in *An Inspector Calls*? List **three**.

**Idea 1:** ..............................

**Idea 2:** ..............................

**Idea 3:** ..............................

Skills boost

## How do I choose precise vocabulary?

You need to choose precise vocabulary in your responses to show full understanding of Priestley's main ideas. To do this, you should build up a bank of ambitious vocabulary for each of the key characters and themes.

**1** These key points relate to ideas about love and relationships in *An Inspector Calls*. For each point, choose one word from the list below and write it below the relevant point. Use at least **one** word from each column.

Choose words that describe love *at that point in the play*. Aim to be as precise as possible.

| Act I | Act II | Act III |
|---|---|---|
| Arthur Birling speaks about the engagement and his business hopes. | Gerald talks about saving Eva from Alderman Meggarty. | Eric says he insisted on going back to Eva's lodgings for sex. |
| | | |
| Gerald defends his lack of attention to Sheila over the summer. | Gerald says Eva loved him and he was the most important person in her life. | Eric says he did not love Eva 'or anything'. |
| | | |
| Sybil Birling warns Sheila that men will always put business first. | Sheila returns Gerald's engagement ring. | Gerald asks Sheila to take the ring back as 'Everything's all right now.' |
| | | |

| | | | |
|---|---|---|---|
| romantic | unequal | hypocritical | damaging |
| arranged | unrealistic | dishonest | exploitative |
| faithfulness | fairy tale | sordid | squalid |
| commitment | contrasting | demanding | dangerous |
| contented | insincere | cruel | manipulative |

**2** Think about the Inspector at key points in the play. For each point, choose one word from the list below and write it below the relevant point.

Try to choose a different word each time so you show a full understanding of every aspect of the Inspector's character.

| Act I | Act II | Act III |
|---|---|---|
| He tells the Birlings that Eva died 'after several hours of agony'. | Sheila warns her mother that the Inspector knows everything. | He warns the Birlings that everybody has a responsibility to care for each other. |
| | | |
| He interrupts Arthur Birling's impatient protest: 'cutting through, massively'. | Sybil Birling says he has made a big impression on the younger generation. | His visit proves to be a hoax. |
| | | |

| | | | |
|---|---|---|---|
| judgemental | powerful | symbolic | commanding |
| mysterious | omniscient | challenging | imposing |
| dominating | distinctive | moral | formidable |
| righteous | prophetic | dramatic | compassionate |

## 2 How do I link my ideas to express them more clearly?

You should use conjunctions to link your ideas, as this will help you to express those ideas more fluently.

**Coordinating** conjunctions link related or contrasting ideas:

*and* *but* *or* *so*

Remember to choose and position your conjunction carefully to express each idea as clearly and fluently as possible.

**Subordinating** conjunctions express more complex connections:

- an explanation – for example: *because* *in order to* *as a result* *consequently*
- a comparison – for example: *although* *however* *on the other hand* *whereas*
- a sequence – for example: *when* *after* *until* *first*

1 Look at these pairs of sentences. Circle (A) the conjunctions in the sentences labelled **B**.

A *Arthur Birling protests about the Inspector's visit. The Inspector interrupts him by 'cutting in'.*

B *When Arthur Birling protests about his visit, the Inspector interrupts him by 'cutting in'.*

A *Sheila realises early in the play that she is partly responsible for Eva's death. Arthur continues to feel that he was justified in treating Eva harshly.*

B *Sheila realises early in the play that she is partly responsible for Eva's death, whereas Arthur continues to feel that he was justified in treating her harshly.*

2 Re-write the following pairs of sentences, using a conjunction to link them.

a *The Inspector questions each of the family in turn.* + *He wants to build up a 'chain of events' that will make them consider their behaviour.*

..........

..........

b *The Inspector challenges Arthur over his treatment of Eva.* + *Arthur tries to justify his decision to dismiss her.*

..........

..........

c *Sheila believes in the idea of romantic love at the start of the play.* + *She is more realistic at the end when she refuses to take back Gerald's ring.*

..........

..........

## 3 How do I extend my sentences to develop my ideas more fully?

One way to extend your sentences and develop your ideas is by using conjunctions. Other ways include using:

- present participles: a verb ending in *-ing*
- the pronoun *which*.

**Conjunctions**

| | | | |
|---|---|---|---|
| and | but | when | as |
| before | after | although | if |
| whereas | unless | because | since |

Look at this sentence:

Arthur boasts about having been a Lord Mayor and an Alderman ...

You could complete it in four ways, using:

- this conjunction → as soon as the Inspector arrives.
- a different conjunction → in order to appear important.
- a present participle → believing it will impress the Inspector.
- *which* → which just makes the Inspector impatient.

1. Complete this sentence in **four** different ways:

Sybil Birling insists the Inspector do his duty ...

a. using a conjunction: ........................................

b. using a different conjunction: ........................................

c. using a present participle: ........................................

d. using *which*: ........................................

2. Annotate this student's sentences to make them a single sentence. Use a present participle or *which*.

a. *The Inspector takes his duties very seriously. This encourages the audience to see him as having high moral standards.*

b. *Sybil Birling is rude to the Inspector and says his comments are 'impertinent'. This creates the impression that she is arrogant.*

3. Re-read all the sentences you have written on this page to check that they are fluently and clearly expressed. Re-write any that are not.

........................................

........................................

........................................

........................................

........................................

........................................

........................................

You can use *which* or a present participle to avoid starting sentences with 'This suggests ...' or 'This shows ...'. For example:

- Gerald was engaged to Sheila when he had an affair with Eva which suggests he had double standards.
- Gerald was engaged to Sheila when he had an affair with Eva, suggesting he had double standards.

# Developing a critical writing style

To express your ideas clearly and precisely, you need to:
- select ambitious vocabulary that expresses your ideas precisely
- use conjunctions, present participles and *which* to link your ideas and express them clearly.

Look again at the **second** exam-style question you saw at the start of the unit.

**Exam-style question**

How does Priestley use the Inspector in *An Inspector Calls* to explore ideas about a fair society?

Write about:
- how Priestley presents the Inspector
- how Priestley uses the Inspector to explore ideas about a fair society. **(30 marks)**

AO4 **(4 marks)**

Look at this short paragraph from one student's response to the question.

*At the start of the play the Inspector is presented as a good character. He is described in the stage directions as giving an impression of 'massiveness'. He is not bothered by Arthur Birling's boasting about being Mayor. Arthur gets impatient with him. Gerald gets annoyed. The Inspector stays cool and speaks 'gravely'. He also interrupts by 'cutting in, massively'. He makes Arthur tell him what he did to Eva. This suggests the Inspector is going to be a big character in the play.*

1 a Underline at least **three** examples of vocabulary that could be more precise.

b Note down in the margin at least **three** alternative vocabulary choices for each one.

c Highlight any sentences you feel should be linked or developed to improve the clarity and precision of the writing.

d Write an improved version of this paragraph, either by adjusting the text above or by re-writing it in the space below.

# Your turn!

You are now going to **write one paragraph** in response to the exam-style question below.

**Exam-style question**

How does Priestley use the Inspector in *An Inspector Calls* to explore ideas about a fair society?

Write about:

- how Priestley presents the Inspector
- how Priestley uses the Inspector to explore ideas about a fair society. **(30 marks)**

**AO4 (4 marks)**

1. What ideas about a fair society does Priestley explore in the play?

   **Idea 1:** ..............................

   ..............................

   **Idea 2:** ..............................

   ..............................

   **Idea 3:** ..............................

   ..............................

   **Idea 4:** ..............................

   ..............................

2. Choose **one** of your ideas and make notes about how the Inspector is used to show this.

3. Now add some ambitious vocabulary to your ideas. Remind yourself of these words to describe the Inspector.

| | | | |
|---|---|---|---|
| judgemental | powerful | symbolic | commanding |
| mysterious | omniscient | challenging | imposing |
| dominating | distinctive | moral | formidable |
| righteous | prophetic | dramatic | compassionate |

4. Use your ideas to write **one** paragraph in response to the exam-style question on paper. Remember to:
   - choose your vocabulary carefully
   - think about ways in which you can link your ideas to develop and express them clearly and precisely.

5. When you have finished, read your paragraph.
   - **a** Underline where you have used ambitious vocabulary.
   - **b** Circle where you have joined sentences effectively.
   - **c** Highlight where you have developed your sentences to make your writing more fluent.

# Review your skills

### Check up

Review your response to the exam-style question on page 71. Tick the column to show how well you think you have done each of the following.

| | Not quite | Nearly there | Got it! |
|---|---|---|---|
| used ambitious vocabulary | | | |
| used conjunctions, present participles and the pronoun *which* to link your ideas and express them clearly | | | |

Look over all of your work in this unit. Note down **three** points to remember when trying to express your ideas as clearly and precisely as possible.

1. ..........
2. ..........
3. ..........

## Need more practice?

You can EITHER:

1. Look again at your paragraph written in response to the exam-style question on page 71. Re-write it, experimenting with different vocabulary choices and sentence structures, linking your ideas in different ways. Which paragraph is most effective in expressing your ideas clearly and precisely?

AND/OR:

2. Write **one** paragraph in response to the exam-style question below. Remember to focus on your vocabulary choices and your sentence structures.

### Exam-style question

How does Priestley explore love in *An Inspector Calls*?

Write about:

- the ideas about love in *An Inspector Calls*
- how Priestley presents these ideas by the ways he writes.

**(30 marks)**

AO4 (4 marks)

How confident do you feel about each of these **skills?** Colour in the bars.

1. How do I choose precise vocabulary?
2. How do I link my ideas to express them more clearly?
3. How do I extend my sentences to develop my ideas more fully?

# Answers

## Unit 1

### Page 2

1. For example:

   **Key point 2:** Mr Birling tries to dominate Eric and treats him like a child by telling him to keep quiet when he interrupts.

   **Key point 3:** Early in Act I, Sheila is more interested in her engagement ring than in serious conversation.

2. For example, points 1, 3, 4 and 5.
3. For example: Sheila refuses to take part in a toast; this shows she is challenging her parents and it highlights the difference between the old and young people's responses to Eva.

### Page 3

1. a 1 – Arthur; 2 – Sheila; 3 – Gerald; 4 – Mrs B; 5 – Eric

   b Eva Smith

   c For example: A relaxed mood is created as the setting is a prosperous dining room, the characters are dressed for dinner and the lighting is 'pink and intimate'. The characters are all happy as they are celebrating Sheila's engagement and are 'pleased with themselves'.

2. a For example: 'Just a knighthood'.

   b Mr Birling is boasting and the word 'just' suggests he hopes for even higher status in the future.

3.

| Order of events | Events | Character responsible |
|---|---|---|
| 3 | Eva changes her name to Daisy Renton and starts a relationship with a man. She moves away when he breaks off the relationship. | Gerald |
| 4 | Eva meets a man in Brumley and gets pregnant. He steals money to support her. | Eric |
| 2 | Eva works at Milwards until she is sacked because of a complaint about her. | Sheila |
| 5 | Eva asks for help from the Brumley Women's Charity but is refused. | Mrs Birling |
| 1 | Eva organises a strike at Birling and Company and is sacked. | Arthur Birling |

### Page 4

1. b For example: The Inspector revealing that Eva was pregnant raises the tension as the audience will start to connect her with Eric – as he is the only family member not to have been questioned and he is not on stage.

2. a 1 = Eric and Mr Birling argue about the stolen money.

   2 = Sheila questions whether Goole was really an Inspector.

   3 = Mr Birling rings Chief Constable Roberts.

   4 = Gerald rings the infirmary.

   b For example: The audience would start to question whether the Inspector was real and would be feeling tension about how the characters will react to the hoax.

### Page 5

1. a A = c, B = a, C = b
2. b For example: The fact that Eric challenges his father over the strike suggests that the traditional age relationships in the play are starting to change, and it is youth that is becoming responsible and mature.
3. b For example: The fact that Eric shows distress and shame over his part in Eva's fate suggests that he has learned from experience and is becoming less immature.

### Page 6

The student has shown a clear focus on the question and shown an understanding of the plot/structure of the play by starting with how Eric is presented at the start and going through the stages of his change. The events selected are the most significant for the question and fully support the points being made.

### Page 7

1. 1 Eric is drunk at the celebratory party.

   2 Mr Birling calls the *Titanic* 'unsinkable'.

   3 Mr Birling is told Eva has killed herself using bleach.

   4 Sheila tells her father not to interfere in her engagement.

   5 Mrs Birling tells Sheila not to contradict her.

   6 Mrs Birling insists the father of the unborn child is to blame.

   7 Sheila accuses her parents of being childish by not facing facts.

   8 Mr Birling relaxes when the Inspector has gone and pours drinks.

   9 Eric agrees with Sheila that their parents' reaction is frightening.

   10 Gerald tries to give back the engagement ring.

2. 2 Mr Birling calls the *Titanic* 'unsinkable'.

   3 Mr Birling is told Eva has killed herself using bleach.

   8 Mr Birling relaxes when the Inspector has gone and pours drinks.

   10 Gerald tries to give back the engagement ring.

3. 7 Sheila accuses her parents of being childish by not facing facts.

   9 Eric agrees with Sheila that their parents' reaction is frightening.

(4) 4 Sheila tells her father not to interfere in her engagement.

7 Sheila accuses her parents of being childish by not facing facts.

9 Eric agrees with Sheila that their parents' reaction is frightening.

# Unit 2

## Page 10

(1) For example: Arthur is shown as the most powerful character as he has the most lines, which suggests he is the most important.

(2) For example: When Arthur jokes about the events it shows he has not taken the Inspector's visit seriously and has learned nothing.

(3) Reputation

## Page 11

(1) All the words are appropriate.

(2) All the words are appropriate.

(3) Mr Birling – arrogant; Eric – shocked; Sheila – sympathetic; Gerald – indifferent

## Page 12

(1) a For example: Wishes she hadn't been told about Eva's death; Warns her mother that the Inspector knows everything; After Inspector goes, criticises parents for not changing

b For example: Sheila's initial reaction to the news about Eva is sympathy, but she soon wishes she hadn't been told. This suggests she is still immature at this point. However, by the end of the play she has learned to take responsibility for her actions and is shocked by her parents' behaviour.

(2) For example: no change – Arthur and Sybil; slight remorse – Gerald; some remorse – Eric; extreme remorse – Sheila.

(3) For example: The Inspector appears mysterious when he shows the photograph and then takes it back as the audience will wonder why he can't show it to all the characters at the same time.

## Page 13

(1) For example: Mr Birling – feels his only duty is to himself, his business and his family; Sybil – shows no sense of responsibility despite running a charity; Sheila – shows she has developed a sense of responsibility as she is able to admit her part in Eva's fate by having her turned her out of a job.

(2) a 'Between us we drove that girl to commit suicide'

b For example: Sheila has developed a sense of social responsibility as she recognises that her family's actions caused Eva's death.

(3) For example: Arthur tells Sybil to thank 'cook' – equality; Arthur expresses regret that Gerald's parents can't be at the party – love; Arthur worries that he will lose his chance of a knighthood – reputation.

## Page 14

(1) a For example: 'Priestley presents Sheila as rather shallow', 'described mainly in terms of her appearance'.

b For example: 'at the start of the play', 'her initial reaction', 'her interest in what happened to Eva intensifies'.

c For example: 'she begins to challenge her father', 'her emerging sense of responsibility'.

d For example: 'wealthy middle class', 'her emerging sense of responsibility'.

(2) For example: **age** and **equality** could be annotated.

# Unit 3

## Page 18

(1) **character**: 'Mr Birling feels his responsibility is to make large profits'

**structure**: 'Inspector questions each character in turn'

(2) 'The Inspector insists Gerald stay while Arthur is questioned.'

## Page 19

(1) b For example: **c** ('Mrs Birling turns Eva away from her charity') can be linked to **B** (morality) because Mrs Birling makes herself morally superior by judging Eva.

(2) b For example:

**Power**: When Arthur says 'a man has to make his own way' he is showing the determination and strength to succeed.

**Morality**: When Arthur says 'you'd think everybody has to look after everybody else ... community and all that nonsense' he is showing that he is really only interested in looking after himself.

## Page 20

(1) a For example: as belonging to the middle classes, negative, dangerous, corrupting and taken for granted.

b For example: When Arthur Birling tells the Inspector that he used to be Lord Mayor he is using his power to try to influence things. This shows power can be corrupting.

(2) a Key event 1 is most relevant as evidence for Statement 1.

b For example: At this point in the play I think Priestley wants the audience to think that the younger generation are more in touch with modern thinking than the older generation, which gives them greater power in the situation.

(3) At the start, power is shown to belong to the middle classes when Arthur boasts about his impending knighthood. However, later in the play, the power shifts from the middle class Birlings to the Inspector and this is shown when he is described as 'taking charge masterfully'.

## Page 21

(1) For example:

Responsibility = Inspector. In Act II, he tells Mrs Birling he will make sure the father of Eva's child is held responsible.

Equality = Eva. In Act I she was unable to fight for a better standard of living as she could not manage with no wages while on strike.

② a They are all appropriate – except, perhaps, responsibility.

b For example: Equality –'EDNA, the parlourmaid, is just clearing the table'

③ For example: Stage 1 – Sheila abused her responsibility as a wealthy middle class woman to get Eva dismissed for no reason.

### Page 22

① For example: Arthur calling people 'cranks'.

② For example: 'At the start of the play, Priestley suggests that the wealthy middle class has no sense of responsibility for others. This is shown through the Birlings, who are presented as wealthy by the comfortable setting'

③ For example: In contrast, the Inspector is used to promote the idea of responsibility as he forces the other characters in turn to face up to their part in Eva's death.

## Unit 4

### Page 26

① For example: 'Represents division of classes at the time'

② For example: Priestley was saying the division of the classes was wrong – Arthur Birling says the working classes should be treated harshly, but he also describes the *Titanic* as 'unsinkable' which implies his views are wrong.

③ For example: modern audiences would find Sybil's reaction to Eric's relationship with Eva strange, as class makes little difference to relationships these days.

### Page 27

① All but 'J.B. Priestley went to university' and 'Captain Scott died in the Antarctic' should be ticked.

② For example: Most married women were dependent on their husbands – Sheila would be dependent on Gerald when they married.

③ For example, answers for Sheila might include:

- She would perhaps have had a job.
- She might have worked during WWII and become more independent.
- She would have been able to vote.

### Page 28

① a Probably '1912 coal miners' strike secured minimum wage'.

b For example: The coal miners' strike scared wealthy businessmen like Arthur who thought they would lose profits.

② a The first point.

b The fact that Sybil defers to her husband is typical of the beliefs about women's place in the Edwardian era: they didn't have the vote and were seen as inferior to men.

③ For example: There was no unemployment benefit so Sybil's charity was Eva's last hope.

### Page 29

① a Paragraphs A and B match all the points.

Paragraph C matches **a** and **e**.

b Paragraph B is the most detailed.

② For example: An audience in 1945 would probably have felt very sorry for Eva but may have shared Sybil's prejudice against single mothers. However, a modern audience would probably be shocked that Eva needed to rely on charity as we now have a welfare state.

### Page 30

① For example:

| | |
|---|---|
| Priestley presents Sybil as feeling no sense of responsibility towards the lower classes.<br>Sybil accepts no blame for her part in Eva's death.<br>She is presented as very judgemental. | makes a clear point about Sybil, linking her to the theme of responsibility |
| She pays no attention to her servant, Edna, unless it is to give her orders and shows no concern for her welfare as she tells her to 'wait up' until she is needed.<br>calling Eva a girl 'of that class' and looking down on her for being single and pregnant.<br>she only helps those she feels have earned it, and feels Eva 'only had herself to blame'. | uses a key event or speech as evidence |
| This reflects Priestley's negative feelings about the way the rich in Edwardian society treated the working classes.<br>Beliefs about the working class had begun to change in 1945, with the introduction of the welfare state | identifies a relevant contextual idea |
| an audience at that time would have been more sympathetic than Sybil about Eva's situation. | comments on audience at the time the play was written |
| A twenty-first century audience would certainly feel Sybil's attitude was wrong and might even see her as cruel. | compares 1945 audience with modern audience response |

## Unit 5

### Page 34

① For example: Characters used to show guilt:

- In Act I Arthur calls his sacking of Eva 'justified'

② For example: **themes** and **context** shown:

Inspector wants each character to take responsibility:

stands for socialist ideas about responsibility – in Act III before he leaves he talks about people being responsible for each other and 'members of one body' – reflects new ideas after WWII.

③ Yes

### Page 35

① The 'Guilt' plan should be labelled 'Points'; the 'Sheila and Gerald' plan should be labelled 'Plot'.

② a/b For example: theme: love – different for men and women

③ For example: Sheila (*excited*): 'Oh – Gerald – you've got it.'

## Page 36

1. a. For example: love/morality
   b. Gerald, Sheila, Eric
2. a. For example: A (exploitation) could link with a, b, c, d and e.
   b. For example: Exploitation can be linked to power as it was Arthur's power as a wealthy businessman that allowed Eva to be exploited for poor wages.
3. a. For example: love
   b. For example: Love can be linked because Arthur seems more interested in Gerald's social status than in his daughter's happiness.

## Page 37

1. a. For example: (clockwise from left)
   By revealing the truth about Eva.
   To force characters to face responsibilities.
   morality
   b. C
2. a. For example: (clockwise from left)
   Yes: responsibility, morality
   To show how it should be used to help others.
   Arthur/Inspector
   a bit of both (positive and negative)
   b. For example: Priestley explores ideas about power in the play by showing how dangerous it is if it is abused and how it should be used responsibly.

## Page 38

1. a. B
   b. For example: 'Sheila begins the play as a rather shallow character.'
   c. For example: Themes: 'This is the first hint in the play that love means different things to men and women.'

# Unit 6

## Page 42

1. For example:
   Structure – 'Stage directions at start – contrast between Edna clearing away and "comfortable" dining room setting; Birlings in evening dress'
   Context – 'Shows inequality before welfare state and gender inequality of time'
   Audience response – 'intended to educate original audience'
2. For example: It links as Sheila and Eric are part of the younger generation and Priestley wanted to show that society could become more equal in the future.

## Page 43

1.

| | |
|---|---|
| He is not intimidated by the Birlings. | ✓ |
| He represents Priestley's ideas about responsibility. | ✓ |
| He challenges the Birlings and Gerald. | ✓ |
| He isn't a real Inspector. | ✗ |
| His visit turns out to be a hoax. | ✗ |
| Edna shows him in. | ✗ |
| He exposes the family's lack of morals. | ✓ |

2.

| | |
|---|---|
| Eva's life is difficult. | ✗ |
| Inequality allows wealthy to exploit w/class. | ✓ |
| The Birlings are wealthy. | ✗ |
| Gerald is superior to the Birlings. | ✗ |
| W/class have fewer opportunities. | ✓ |
| The Birlings benefit from inequality. | ✓ |

## Page 44

1. a. Point 1 = E; Point 2 = B; Point 3 = D
   b. For example: Evidence E supports Point 1 because Mrs B showed no compassion for Eva even after hearing about her fate, but the audience would be shocked.
2. For example, Point 1 with evidence E links to context as it shows how difficult life was for working classes with no welfare state.

## Page 45

1. For example: B, A, C, D (this is the order the events happen in the play so it shows understanding of the structure.)
2. a. For example: B, A and C, D (this sequence starts with the Birlings who benefit from inequality, then goes to Eva who is harmed by inequality, then on to another point about Eva and ends with ideas about how things could be different.)
   b. For example: B, A, C, D (this order starts with the way some people benefit from the middle classes and then moves on to those who don't.)

## Page 46

1. For example: 'the stage directions describe him as creating an impression of "massiveness".'
2. Structure – 'Priestley first suggests he is powerful as the stage directions...'
   Context and audience response – 'surprised an audience in 1945, as wealthy families were used to commanding respect at that time.'
3. A chronologically

# Unit 7

## Page 50

1. For example:
   - Quotation: 'hard school of business'.
   - Audience: 'would suggest to the audience that he is about to say something important'.
   - Language: 'the use of the imperative "listen" after the word "Now" shows he feels in charge.'
   - Stage directions: 'Arthur dismisses his worries and relaxes ... "jovially".'
2. For example: When he calls the Inspector a 'crank' after he has left.

## Page 51

1. a. For example: 'Just let me finish'/'You've a lot to learn'
   b. For example: 'I'm talking as a hard-headed, practical man'/'And I say'

2 a For example: 'damn you, damn you'

b For example: The words 'damn you, damn you' suggest the relationship has broken down as it is a very threatening way to speak to your mother.

3 a For example: 'damned exasperating'/'They just won't try to understand'

b For example: 'a lot of stuff'/'downright public scandal'

## Page 52

1 tense or anxious

2 Either of the following.

They would feel satisfied as she deserves to be punished.

They would hate her for what she did to Eva.

3 For example: 'understanding now'/'thunderstruck'

4 For example: He keeps Eric away so that the audience know more than Eric when he comes back. This increases the tension as the audience will want to know how he will respond before they decide whether he is guilty or not.

## Page 53

1 A c
B b
C f
D a
E d
F e

2 For example: Arthur speaks to both Sybil and Sheila in short imperatives, but speaks 'very sharply' to Sheila, whereas he softens his voice to be 'gentler' with Sybil. This shows he feels very challenged by Sheila but still protective of his wife.

## Page 54

1

| key point focusing on the key words in the question | At the end of the play Priestley uses the relationship between Arthur and Eric to show how little the older generation has learned about morals and responsibility. |
|---|---|
| short quotations as evidence | 'hold your tongue' |
| stage directions used as evidence | 'threatening', |
| some link to the context of the play | the traditional expectation of respect for the older generation is being ignored |
| some reference to the specific type of language or language features used | the imperative idiom |
| a comment on the effect of language choice(s) | creates a very aggressive image and shows how angry he is |
| a comment on the effect of structural choice(s) | which suggests he feels he has lost control of his relationship with his son |
| a comment on the audience's reaction to the form of the play | This aggression would cause the audience to be openly judgemental about Arthur as it shows he has learned nothing from the experience with the Inspector; he is still more concerned about himself. |

# Unit 8

## Page 58

| Eva Smith is used by Priestley to represent the working classes and show how easily they were exploited by the wealthy. | a point that links to the question |
|---|---|
| For example, she is not seen on stage, she is only described by others. | evidence about how a character is presented |
| This is important as it shows how wealthy families like the Birlings rely on the working classes without ever really seeing them as real people. | explanation of evidence |
| This reflects the gap between the upper and lower classes in Edwardian society. | link between explanation and context |

| Eva Smith is first presented to the audience through Arthur Birling in a positive way. | a clear point |
|---|---|
| This is shown when Arthur praises her, calling her a 'lively good-looking girl' and a 'good worker'. | evidence |
| This suggests he thought she was a good employee. | explanation of effect |
| This was not unusual, as many factories liked employing women in 1912 as women could be paid less and were not under the protection of trade unions. This meant that if the women protested about their low pay, they could easily be sacked. | link between explanation and context |
| This is shown in the play when Arthur talks of Eva being sacked for having 'a lot to say – far too much'. | how context is shown in play |
| He also describes her as one of the 'ring-leaders'. | extra detail |
| This shows his distrust of the working classes as it has connotations of illegality or criminal activity. | analysis of language in extra detail |

## Page 59

1 a For example: Arthur uses the metaphor 'bees in a hive' to describe a society where people look after each other. This shows his negative feelings about a society where the classes mix as it creates an image of thousands of people crowded on top of each other.

b Arthur tells Gerald and Eric to 'take my word for it' and refers to them as 'youngsters'. The use of an imperative sentence suggests he is used to being listened to, and the patronising term 'youngsters' suggests he feels superior to them.

c It is important as it foreshadows the dramatic impact he will have and suggests he is more important than what Arthur is saying.

## Page 60

1 A and C both link well.

② Contextual example: This reflects the fact that middle class men in the Edwardian era would have viewed working class girls like Eva as beneath them and therefore it did not matter how badly they were treated.

Audience example: A modern audience would find these comments very offensive as there is more gender equality these days and men are expected to treat women with respect.

### Page 61

① a *This is first shown when Eric criticises his father for sacking Eva and then* when Sheila interrupts Arthur by 'cutting in' to his suggestion that he talk the matter over privately with the Inspector.

b Priestley's use of the harsh verb 'cutting' for the stage direction suggests Sheila has started to lose respect for her father at this point.

② First interpretation = 'The use of the phrase "labour costs" suggests that he sees his employees as just a resource to be used.'

Additional interpretation = 'The word "costs" also suggests his annoyance at having to pay them.'

③ Eva must have been really desperate to kill herself in such a horrible way. It also suggests that Eva wanted to make herself clean again after her dealings with the Birlings, as disinfectant has connotations of killing harmful germs.

## Unit 9

### Page 66

① For example: 'committed', 'unease', 'qualms'

② For example: 'and', 'while', 'when'

③ For example: For example, her first speech is directed to be spoken 'gaily', however, it is also supposed to be said 'possessively'.

④ For example:

**Idea 1:** Love is shown to be damaging to Eva.

**Idea 2:** Arthur sees the marriage as a business match – not a love match.

**Idea 3:** Love is seen differently by men and women.

### Page 67

| | | |
|---|---|---|
| Arthur Birling speaks about the engagement and his business hopes. *arranged* | Gerald talks about saving Eva from Alderman Meggarty. *squalid* | Eric says he insisted on going back to Eva's lodgings for sex. *sordid* |
| Gerald defends his lack of attention to Sheila over the summer. *dishonest* | Gerald says Eva loved him and he was the most important person in her life. *fairy tale* | Eric says he did not love Eva 'or anything'. *exploitative* |
| Sybil Birling warns Sheila that men will always put business first. *unequal* | Sheila returns Gerald's engagement ring. *commitment* | Gerald asks Sheila to take the ring back as 'Everything's all right now.' *hypocritical* |

②

| | | |
|---|---|---|
| He tells the Birlings Eva died 'after several hours of agony'. *compassionate/ judgemental* | Sheila warns her mother that the Inspector knows everything. *omniscient* | He warns the Birlings that everybody has a responsibility to care for each other. *prophetic/ symbolic* |
| He interrupts Arthur Birling's impatient protest: 'cutting through, massively'. *powerful/ formidable* | Sybil Birling says he has made a big impression on the younger generation. *commanding/ imposing* | His visit proves to be a hoax. *mysterious/ symbolic* |

### Page 68

① 'When', 'whereas'

② For example:

a The Inspector questions each of the family in turn *in order to* build up a 'chain of events' that will make them consider their behaviour.

b The Inspector challenges Arthur over his treatment of Eva, *but* Arthur tries to justify his decision to dismiss her.

c Sheila believes in the idea of romantic love at the start of the play, *although* she is more realistic at the end when she refuses to take back Gerald's ring.

### Page 69

① a Sybil Birling insists the Inspector do his duty and find the father of Eva's child.

b Sybil Birling insists the Inspector do his duty, because she thinks the child's father is to blame.

c Sybil Birling insists the Inspector do his duty, believing that the father of Eva's baby is to blame rather than her.

d Sybil Birling insists the Inspector do his duty, which is ironic as the father is Eric.

② a The Inspector takes his duties very seriously, encouraging the audience to see him as having high moral standards.

b Sybil Birling is rude to the Inspector and says his comments are 'impertinent', which creates the impression that she is arrogant.

### Page 70

① For example:

a / b good [powerful, formidable, impressive]; bothered [intimidated, phased, overawed]; stays [remains]; big [important, significant]

c / d At the start of the play the Inspector is presented as a <u>powerful</u> character *as* he is described in the stage directions as giving an impression of 'massiveness' *and* he is not <u>intimidated</u> by Arthur's boasting about being Mayor. Arthur gets impatient with him *and* Gerald gets annoyed, *whereas* the Inspector <u>remains</u> cool and speaks 'gravely'. He also interrupts by 'cutting in, massively', *demanding* Arthur tell him what he did to Eva, *which* suggests the Inspector is going to be a <u>significant</u> character in the play.

# Notes

# Notes

# Notes

# Notes

# Notes

# Notes